Long-face Jumeau
24" Tall
Photo by Howard Foulke

# BLUE BOOK
## OF
# DOLLS AND VALUES

A GUIDE TO IDENTIFICATION

**Edited by:**
**Thelma Bateman**
**Jan Foulke**

**Published by**
**HOBBY HOUSE PRESS**
**4701 Queensbury Road**
**Riverdale, Maryland 20840**

Photography by:
Thelma Bateman
Howard Foulke


Production Assistants:
Laurie DeGarie
Beth Foulke
Carolyn Receveur
Diane Ruddell
Mary Ruddell
Julia Shockley


© 1974, Hobby House Press
ISBN 0-87588-080-0

We are grateful to the following collectors who so willingly shared their collections with us. The dolls pictured were a part of these collections when photographed.

PHOTOGRAPHS OF HOWARD FOULKE

Joyce Alderson Collection. Illus. Nos. 11, 22, 106, 174, 186

Sandy Contarino Collection. Illus. No. 108

Beth Foulke Collection. Illus. Nos. 7, 96, 152

H&J Foulke Collection. Illus. Nos. 2, 3, 4, 5, 10, 16, 25, 28, 29, 66 72, 102, 103, 104, 109, 128, 150, 151, 153, 160, 169

Cecelia Geppi Collection. Illus. Nos. 15A, 146

Betty Harms Collection. Illus. Nos. 8, 179

Arlene Krenz Collection. Illus. Nos. 119

Emily Manning Collection. Illus. Nos. 15, 97, 124

Carol Smith Collection. Illus. No. 35

Helen Teske Collection. Illus. Nos. 26, 58, 63, 76, 91, 92, 100, 139, 158, 161, 164, 172, 173

Emma Wedmore Collection. Illus. Nos. 181, 182, 183, 184

Richard Wright Collection. Illus. Nos. 1, 6, 21, 78, 84, 88, 93, 98, 113, 118, 120, 144, 154, 168, 170, 176

PHOTOGRAPHS OF THELMA BATEMAN

Arkin Collection. Illus. No. 60

Thelma Bateman. Illus. Nos. 12, 13, 17, 18, 20, 31, 36, 79, 94, 121, 123, 132, 133, 136, 137, 138, 166, 167, 175, 177, 180, 185, 192, 193

Brand Collection. Illus. No. 27

Carter Craft Dollhouse Collection. Illus. Nos. 23, 24, 32, 33, 34, 38 39, 56, 57, 61, 64, 65, 67, 69, 73, 75, 81, 82, 83, 85, 90, 95, 105, 107, 112, 114, 115, 116, 125, 130, 140, 142, 143, 145, 149, 155, 157, 159, 162, 188, 189, 190, 192, 194

Darby Collection. Illus. Nos. 53, 111, 129

Dorothy Coleman Collection. Illus. Nos. 9, 14, 30, 40, 41, 42, 43, 44, 46, 47, 48, 49, 50, 51, 52, 55, 59, 68, 70, 71, 74, 77, 80, 86, 87, 89, 99, 101, 110, 117, 120, 131, 134, 135, 147, 148, 163, 165, 171, 178, 187,

Kahler Collection. Illus. No. 156

Long Collection. Illus. No. 45

Morley Collection. Illus. No. 19

Roberts Collection. Illus. No. 54

Salatich Collection. Illus. No. 126

Sigrud Collection. Illus. No. 122

# PREFACE
By Thelma Bateman

First, let me say that the doll prices given within this book
are intended as value guides rather than arbitrarily set prices.
Each doll price recorded here is actually a compilation. The
retail prices in this book are recorded as accurately as possible
but in the case of errors, typographical, clerical or otherwise,
the author and publisher assume no liability nor responsibility
for any loss incurred by users of this book.

Important help in doing this volume was generously given by
several people including the publisher Paul A. Ruddell, whose
idea it was in the first place. Help of all kinds came from
Dorothy Smith Coleman of Washington, DC. whose many author-
itative books and articles on antique dolls (done in collaboration
with daughters Elizabeth Ann and Evelyn Jane) are so well
known among doll collectors and museums in this country as
well as abroad.

Much valuable help and needed encouragement was given me
by Mr. and Mrs. Ed. Carter of CARTER CRAFT DOLL HOUSE
Hyattsville, Maryland.

Mrs. George Kahler of Falls Church, Va. kindly loaned
"Scootles" and Mrs. Arlo H. Darby graciously loaned three
dolls to illustrate parts of this book.

Credit is also given for present ownership and permission to
use photographs of a dozen or so dolls who were photographed
long ago. The uncredited dolls are from my own collection.

"Thank Yous" for help received from my generous friends and
also to all those who have been researching for years and
sharing their finds with us all.

Thelma Bateman

Publishers postscript: Unfortunately Mrs. Bateman suffered ill-
health and was unable to continue her work and finish the manu-
script. She is presently convalescing. She is certainly grateful
for prayers from her many doll friends.

# PREFACE

By Jan Foulke

In editing and completing the BLUE BOOK OF DOLLS AND VALUES, I have adhered to Thelma Bateman's original objectives. First, she wanted a book which would help collectors identify dolls and learn more about them:dolls which they already own, those that they might like to own among the large variety pictured, those that are offered to them for purchase, or those which they just might be curious about. Second,she wanted to list the actual retail prices of the dolls discussed. This book achieves both of those objectives.

Dolls are listed alphabetically in the text by the name of the individual doll, the maker, or the type of doll. An extensive index has been provided at the back of the book for the reader's convenience in locating a specific doll. Of course, it would be impossible to include every doll in a volume of this size, but we have tried to include those which were either available, desirable, interesting or popular. For each doll, we have provided historical information, a description of the doll, and in most cases, a photograph.

The historical information given for each doll would have been much more difficult to compile were it not for the original research already published by Dorothy, Elizabeth, & Evelyn Coleman and Johana G. Anderton. For this, we are indebted to them.

Also a debt is owed to those who allowed us to photograph their dolls. We appreciate their cooperation and specifically acknowledge their contribution in the photo credit page.

The data on the prices were gathered from April to August 1974 from antique shops, doll shops, antique shows, advertisements in collectors' periodicals, lists from doll dealers, and purchases reported by friends. It was sorted, indexed, catalogued and finally computed into the range of prices shown in this book. Hence, the figures used here are not our own valuations and judgments--they are the results of our research as to the actual retail prices at which these dolls were either sold or offered for sale. For comparative purposes, we have included where available the prices that Mrs. Bateman compiled in 1970.

In setting down a price, we used a range to allow for the variables discussed later which necessarily affect the price of any doll. All prices given for antique dolls are for those in good to better condition, but showing normal wear, unless specifically noted in the description accompanying that particular doll. The especially outstanding doll in absolutely mint condition, never played with, in the original box, or with original tagged clothes, would command a price far higher than those quoted. Prices given for modern dolls were for those in excellent condition with original hair and clothes except as noted. Again a never-played-with doll in original box would bring a higher priced than noted.

Certain dolls are becoming increasingly difficult to find and are seldom offered at a show or advertised since most dealers usually have a list of customers waiting for these desirable dolls. If we did not find a sufficient number of these dolls offered to be sure of giving a reliable range, we reported the information which we could find and noted the lack on each. In a very few instances we could find none of a certain doll offered, so we resorted to estimates from reliable, established dealers and collectors. These, too, are noted individually.

Our column in THE DOLL READER, a periodical published by Hobby House Press, will try to note any marked changes in doll prices and will sometimes feature dolls which we could not include in this book either because they were not available or because we did not have sufficient space.

No price guide is the final word--it can't provide the absolute answer of what to pay. Use it only as an aid in purchasing a doll. The final decision must be yours, for only you are on the scene actually examining the specific doll in question.

And so, with these last thoughts, we present to you this first edition of the BLUE BOOK OF DOLLS AND VALUES.

Jan Foulke
August 1974

# DETERMINING DOLL PRICES

By Jan Foulke

Adding another doll to your collection is exciting, but it is not as easy as it seems because you must consider so many variable factors before deciding whether or not you should buy a doll and if it is worth the price the seller is asking. Some of these factors have already been outlined by Janet Johl and Dorothy Coleman, but they are important enough to bear restatement and amplification. Hopefully, you will find in this chapter some helpful suggestions about what to look for and what to consider in purchasing a doll.

I have found very few people who buy dolls strictly as an investment. Although many collectors rationalize their purchases by saying that they are making a good investment, they are still actually buying the doll because they like it--it has appeal to them for some reason: perhaps as an object of artistic beauty, perhaps because it evokes some kind of sentiment, perhaps it fills some need that they feel, or perhaps it speaks to something inside them. When my daughter and I go doll shopping, we look at them all, but we only stop to examine closely and consider buying those which have some appeal for us. Thus, we more often find ourselves buying first with our hearts and second with our heads. Anyway, it is this personal feeling toward the doll that makes it of value to you.

After you decide that you like a doll, find out what it is. Certainly, the marks on dolls are important in determining a price for with a little luck, they might tell what the doll is, who made it, where, and sometimes when. A 20" tall doll marked A. M. 390 even though she is in good condition and well dressed, is plentiful and should not cost as much as the harder-to-find S & H 1279 girl in the same size and condition. Likewise, if the doll is marked "Margaret O'Brien, " you know it's a rare one; a "Patsy" would be far more common. Of course, many dolls are unmarked, but after you have seen quite a few dolls, you begin to notice their individual and special characteristics, so that then you can often determine what a doll probably is.

But even the mark doesn't tell all. Two dolls from exactly the same mold could carry vastly different prices (and look entirely different) because of the quality of the work done on the doll.

To command top price, a bisque doll should have lovely bisque, decoration, eyes, and hair. For instance, the quality of the bisque should be smooth and silky, not grainy, rough, peppered (tiny black specks), or pimply. The tinting should be subdued and even, not harsh and splotchy, although the amount of color acceptable is often a matter of personal preference, some collectors liking very pale white bisque and others preferring a little more pink. Since doll heads are hand painted, one of good quality should show artistic skill in the portrayal of the expression on the face and in details, such as the mouth, eyebrows and eyelashes. On a doll with molded hair, deep molding, an unusual hair style, and brush marks to give the hair a more realistic look, would be details which are desirable. If a doll has a wig, the hair should be appropriate, if not original--a lovely human hair wig or good quality mohair. Natural and life-like eyes, whether they are glass or painted, would complete the face. If a doll doesn't meet these standards, it should be priced lower than one that does.

Another factor which is important when pricing a doll, is the condition. A doll with a hairline crack on the face or extensive professional repair would sell for considerably less than a doll with only normal wear; a hairline or a professional repair in an inconspicuous place would decrease the value somewhat, but not nearly so much. You almost have to expect an old doll to show minor wear; perhaps there's a rub on the nose (a vulnerable spot), wear on the hair of an old papier-mâche or china head doll, or scuffed toes or missing fingers on an old composition body--these are to be expected and do not affect the value of the doll. Certainly, an old doll in never-played-with condition, all original hair and clothes, labeled, in its original box is every collector's dream--and would carry the highest of all prices for that type. Unless the doll is rare and you particularly want it, do not pay top price for a doll which needs extensive work; restringing, setting eyes, replacing body parts, new wig, dressing--all these repairs add up to a considerable sum at the doll hospital. As for the composition dolls, you should expect a more nearly perfect condition if you are paying top price--original hair, clothes, little or no crazing, good coloring, tag, if possible. However, dolls in this condition are becoming harder to find. Pay less for a doll which doesn't have original clothes; even less for a damaged one. On the hard plastics and vinyl, you should expect mint condition for top price; original clothes would be a must.

Check over the body of the doll. For a top price, an old doll should have the original or an appropriate old body in good condition. Minor damage or repair to an old body scarcely affects the value of the doll. An original body carefully repaired is preferable to a new one. A good quality ball-jointed composition body is more desirable than a crudely made five-piece body or a stick-type body with just pieces of wood for upper arms and legs. Occasionally the body adds value to the head. For instance, a small six-inch doll with a completely jointed body, or a French fashion with jointed wood body, or a doll with a lady-type body, or a doll with a jointed-toddler-type body would all be more desirable because of their bodies. On the all-composition dolls a body in poor condition, cracked and peeling, greatly reduces the value of the doll.

Look at the clothing critically in considering the value of the doll. It should be appropriate for the doll, made in types of fabrics and styles which would have been in vogue when the doll was produced. Original clothes are, of course, highly desirable and even carefully mended clothes would be preferable to new clothes. However, it is often difficult to determine whether or not the clothes are original or simply just old. Many old dolls came undressed or clad only in a chemise and were dressed at home. A doll with original clothes is certainly more valuable, but whether or not these clothes are retained on the doll seems to be a matter of personal preference among collectors, many of whom enjoy dressing their own dolls. If you do feel that you want to redress your dolls, show respect for the original clothes and keep them in a labeled-bag or box for giving to the next owner should you ever sell your doll, or pass it down to a younger member of the family, for dolls are heirlooms and you are only the keeper for a short time in history.

Take into account the size of the doll in determining the price. Usually price and size are related for a certain type of doll--a smaller size is lower, a larger size is higher. The greatest variances of price to size occur at the extremes, either a very small or a very large doll. On the large side, bisque head dolls, especially over 33" are in demand and rising in price; the large 36" vinyl Shirley Temple and the 30" composition Patsy Mae are practically unavailable. On the tiny side, the small closed-mouth Jumeau and Wee Patsy are examples in the opposite direction, bringing higher prices than comparable average-sized dolls.

A final point to consider in pricing your doll is the age of the doll. An early Queen Anne wood doll would be more greatly valued than a late 19th Century penny wooden. However, curiously enough to some, the oldest dolls do not necessarily command the highest prices. A lovely old china head with exquisite work and very unusual hair-do would bring a good price, but not as much as a 20th Century S.F.B.J. 252 Pouty. Many desirable composition dolls of 1930's are selling at prices higher than older bisque dolls of 1900-1920. So, in determining price the age of the doll, may or may not be significant, according to the specific type.

So far, except for the aspect of personal appeal, the factors which we have considered in pricing a doll have been physical and tangible--the marks, the quality of craftsmanship, condition, clothing, size, and age. But there are still several others; perhaps these might be called the intangible factors to you.

Perhaps most important here would be the availability of the doll--how easy or difficult it is to find. Each year brings more new doll collectors than it brings newly-discovered desirable old dolls; hence, the supply is diminished. As long as the demand for certain antique and collectible dolls is greater than the supply, prices will rise. This explains the gigantic increase in the prices of less common dolls, such as the Brus, K(star)R and S.F.B.J. characters, and googlies, and the more gentle rise in dolls which are fairly common, primarily, the German girl or child dolls. The price you pay should be consistent with the availability of the doll.

Sometimes, however, it is the popularity of a certain doll which makes the price rise. This is currently true with dolls such as Shirley Temple and the Bye-lo baby which still seem to

be fairly plentiful, yet rising in price, because they are popular
and many collectors want them enough to be willing to pay a
price that might be higher than the availability factor warrants.

Of course, another important factor which helps determine
what price goes on the doll in the shop, is the price the dealer
had to pay for it. In buying a doll, a dealer has to consider every-
thing discussed here, in addition to whether or not there is the
possibility of making a reasonable profit on the doll. Contrary to
what many collectors believe, dealers in antique dolls do not
make enormous profits. Their margin of profit is not nearly so
high as that of the proprietor of a shop which sells new items.
This is primarily due to the availability factor already discussed.
Old dolls cannot be ordered from a wholesale catalogue. Fewer
are turning up in attics. Most are coming from collections,
whose owners, understandably enough, want to get as much as
they can for their dolls. To the price which he must pay a dealer
adds his percentage of profit and comes up with a dollar amount
for the tag.

The last factor to consider about doll prices is that the price
guide gives the retail price of a doll if obtained from a dealer,
whereas actually a doll might have several types of buying
prices. This idea is pointed out by Ceil Chandler. First, a dealer
when buying stock could not pay the prices listed; he must buy
somewhat lower if he expects to sell at a profit. In order to
obtain stock, a dealer looks to private individuals who may have
dolls in an attic (and there are fewer and fewer of these with truly
desirable dolls), auctions, collectors, and other dealers as
possible sources--all of which are also available to collectors
who can purchase from these sources at the same prices that
dealers can. Second, a dealer would expect to pay less per doll if
he bought a collection or a large lot than if he purchased them
individually. A third type of price would prevail if a collector
buys from another collector; in this case, you would probably
pay less than when buying from a dealer. The fourth type of
price is the "lucky" price you might find at a shop, garage sale,
flea market, or just about anywhere that there might be an old
doll.

Hopefully, in this chapter, we have presented some ideas which

might be of help to you in purchasing your next doll or in eval-
uating dolls which you already own. And we hope that you will
enjoy many, many hours of pleasure as you build your doll
collection.

Jan Foulke
August 1974

A regular column in THE DOLL READER will be en-
titled "Identifying and Pricing Your Dolls" by Jan Foulke.
This column will keep you abreast of marked price
changes on dolls included in this book. Additional dolls
not covered in this book will appear with complete back-
ground material and a price range. Therefore you will
have the opportunity to identify and price other dolls!
This book is not a static identification and pricing guide--
but a continually updated and expanded guide. Besides
the "Identifying and Pricing Your Dolls" column there
many other features of THE DOLL READER including
articles on: dollmaking, doll collecting, patterns for doll
clothes, miniatures making and collecting and many other
facets of the doll world. THE DOLL READER is indeed
a "Clearinghouse for Information on Dolls".

SUBSCRIBE TODAY! Issued quarterly--March, June,
September, December. $2.95 per year.

DOLL READER
4701 Queensbury Road
Riverdale, MD. 20840

MAKER: Various German firms
DATE: Ca. 1910
MATERIAL: Bisque
MARK: Some with "Germany" and/or numbers
SIZE: Various

---

All-bisque Baby Marked Germany: Jointed at shoulders and hips, curved arms and legs, molded and painted hair, painted eyes, very good workmanship, not dressed; all in good condition.

| | Size 3-4" | $ 35-40 |
| --- | --- | --- |
| | 5" | 45-50 |
| | 6" | 60-70 |

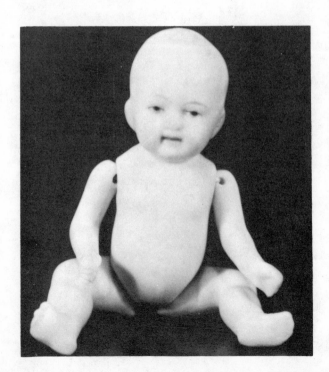

Illus. No. 1
All-Bisque
Baby
"Germany"
5" tall

# ALL-BISQUE BABY DOLLS
### (Made in Japan)

MAKER: Various Japanese firms
DATE: Ca. 1915 – on
MATERIAL: Bisque
MARK: "JAPAN" or "NIPPON"
SIZE: Various small sizes

---

All-bisque Baby Doll Marked "NIPPON" or "JAPAN": Jointed at
shoulders and hips; molded and painted hair and eyes, not
dressed; all in good condition.

Illus. No. 2
Black Baby
"Made in Japan"
4" tall
**All original**

Black Bisque 4" $ 15-20

White Bisque 4"   10-15

# ALL-BISQUE CHARACTERS
### (Made in Japan)

MAKER: Various Japanese firms
DATE: Ca. 1920 - on
MATERIAL: Bisque
MARK: "Made in Japan"
SIZE: Various small sizes

---

All-bisque Characters: Made in an abundant variety. Completely
molded including clothes; all in good condition.

| | | |
|---|---|---|
| Illus. No. 3 | Size 4" | $ 5.00 - 6.00 |
| All-Bisque Characters | 3" | 3.00 - 4.00 |
| "Made in Japan" | | |
| 4" tall | | |

# ALL-BISQUE CHARACTERS
### (Nodding Heads, Molded Clothes)

MAKER: Various German firms
DATE: Ca. 1920
MATERIAL: Bisque
MARK: Germany
SIZE: Up to 4-1/4"

---

All-Bisque Characters: Nodding heads (elastic strung), molded
   clothes; all in good condition.        Size 3"        $ 15-20
Same as above of comic strip or movie characters, such as
   "Our Gang", "Skeezix", "Moon Mullins", etc.        Size 4"
   $ 25-30

Illus. No. 4
All-Bisque
Nodders
3" tall

MAKER: Various German firms
DATE: Ca. 1880 - on
MATERIAL: Bisque
MARK: Some with "Germany" and/or numbers
SIZE: Various

---

All-bisque German Doll: Jointed at shoulders and hips, stationary neck, glass eyes, good wig, closed or open mouth,
molded and painted shoes and stockings; dressed or undressed; all in good condition.

| Illus. No. 5 | Size 4-6" | $ 60- 85 |
| All-Bisque Child Doll | 7-8" | 100-125 |

160
3/0
5-3/4" tall

# ALL-BISQUE CHILD DOLL
### (Molded Clothes)

MAKER: Various German firms
DATE: Ca. 1880 - on
MATERIAL: Bisque
MARK: Usually only numbers
SIZE: Various

---

All-bisque with molded clothes: Jointed only at shoulders,
molded and painted clothes or underwear; molded and
painted hair sometimes with molded hat; painted eyes,
closed mouth, molded shoes and socks (if in underwear often
barefoot); good quality work; all in good condition.

| Illus. No. 6 | Size 4" | $ 45-55 |
|---|---|---|
| All-Bisque Child | 5" | 65-75 |
| Buster Brown-type | 7-1/2" | 125 |
| 5-1/2" tall | | |

# ALL-BISQUE CHILD DOLL
### (Painted Eyes)

MAKER: Various German firms
DATE: Ca. 1880 - on
MATERIAL: Bisque
MARK: Some with "Germany" and/or numbers
SIZE: Various

---

All-bisque German Doll: Jointed at shoulders and hips, stationary neck, painted eyes, painted hair, molded and painted
shoes and stockings, closed mouth, good quality work,
dressed or undressed; all in good condition. Size 4-6"
$ 35-45

Same as above, but with wig instead of painted hair. Size 4-
6"        $ 50-65

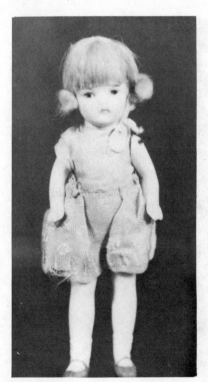

Illus. No. 7
All-Bisque Child Doll
"Germany"
3-1/2" tall

# ALL-BISQUE CHILD DOLL
### (Swivel Neck)

MAKER: Various German and French firms
DATE: Ca. 1880 - on
MATERIAL: Bisque
MARK: Usually only numbers
SIZE: Various

---

All-bisque Swivel-neck Doll: Jointed at neck, shoulders and
hips; glass eyes, good wig, closed or open mouth, molded
shoes or boots and stockings; dressed or undressed; all in
good condition.

|          | Size 4-5" | $ 150-175 |
|----------|-----------|-----------|
|          | 5-6"      | 200-275   |
|          | 7-9"      | 250-300   |

Illus. No. 8
All-Bisque Child Doll
Swivel Neck
8-1/2" tall

# ALL-BISQUE CHILD DOLLS
## (Made in Japan)

MAKER: Various Japanese firms
DATE: Ca. 1915 - on
MATERIAL: Bisque
MARK: "JAPAN" or "NIPPON"
SIZE: Various small sizes

---

All-bisque Child Doll  Marked "Nippon" or "Japan": Jointed at
  shoulders only; molded and painted hair and eyes; may
  have ribbed socks and one-strap shoes; not dressed; all in
  good condition.

| | |
|---|---|
| Size 5-6" | $ 15-25* |
| 7-8" | 25-35 |

*Allow extra for hip joint

```
1970 Price Comparison
Child Doll 4-1/2 - 8"
        $11
```

Marked:"Baby Darling"
  5-1/2" $25-35
Betty Boop type
  5-7" $10-15

Illus. No. 9
Left:
"Nippon" 4-1/2"
    tall
Right:
"Made in Japan"
5-3/4" tall

# ALL-BISQUE DISNEY CHARACTERS
## (Made in Japan)

MAKER: Unknown
DATE: Ca. 1930
MATERIAL: Bisque
MARK: "Made in Japan ©  Walt E. Disney" with name of
  character usually on front
SIZE: Various small sizes

---

All-bisque Disney Characters: Marked as above, molded and
  painted clothes; all in good condition.

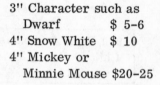

3" Character such as
  Dwarf          $ 5-6
4" Snow White    $ 10
4" Mickey or
  Minnie Mouse $20-25

Illus. No. 10
"Mickey Mouse
Made in Japan
S1271
©Walt E. Disney"

# ALT, BECK & GOTTSCHALCK
## (Bent-Limb Character Baby)

MAKER: Alt, Beck & Gottschalck, Nauendorf, Thüringia,
    Germany
DATE: Ca. 1910 on –
MATERIAL: Bisque head, composition bent-limb body

MARK:        "Made in Germany"
                (Numbers, such as 1361 found underneath
                    mark)

SIZE: Various

---

Marked ABG Baby: Bisque head, open mouth, sleep eyes, good
    wig, open nostrils, bent-limb composition body, suitably
    dressed; nice condition.          Size 15"       $155-175
                                           19-22"       225

Same as above, but with toddler body     Size 15-18"      $175-250

> 1970 Price Comparison
> 16" to 20"     $68

For picture see DOLL STUFF, AGAIN by Elizabeth Andrews
Fisher, page 247

# ALT, BECK & GOTTSCHALCK
## (Child Doll)

MAKER: Alt, Beck & Gottschalck, Nauendorf, Thüringia, Germany

DATE: Ca. 1893 on -

MATERIAL: Bisque heads, composition ball-jointed bodies

MARK:  "Made in Germany"
(Numbers, such as 1362, underneath mark)

SIZE: Various

---

Marked Child Doll: Bisque head, good wig, sleep eyes, open mouth, ball-jointed body, dressed, all in good shape.

Size 20-25"    $120-155

```
1970
Price Comparison
Size 18-36"  $68
```

Illus. No. 11
"ABG
1362
Made in Germany"
24" tall

MAKER: Barr Rubber Products Co., Sandusky, Ohio, U.S.A.
DATE: 1949
MATERIAL: Rubber
MARK: "Columbia Broadcasting System, Inc. Designed by Ruth
   E. Newton"
SIZE: Various
DESIGNER: Ruth E. Newton

---

Amosandra Marked Rubber Baby: Adorable jointed bent-limb
   baby doll, original clothes; all in good condition. Size 9-12"
   $12.50-18.00

| 1970 Price Comparison |
|---|
| Size 9-12"        $15 |

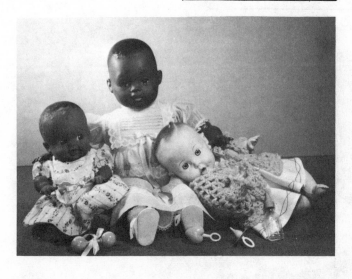

Illus. No. 12
Left: "Amosandra ©    Middle:      Right:
Columbia Broadcasting Ideal's "Saralee" Sun Rubber's "Gerber
     System, Inc.              Baby"
Designed by Ruth E.
Newton" 7" seated

# ANNE SHIRLEY
## (EFFanBEE)

MAKER: EFFanBEE Doll Corp. (Fleischaker & Baum), New
York, N.Y., U.S.A.
DATE: 1935 to ca. 1948
MATERIAL: Composition
MARK: "EFFanBEE ANNE SHIRLEY" embossed across back of
shoulders
SIZE: Various

---

Anne Shirley Doll: All composition Anne Shirley, marked; sleep
eyes, closed mouth, original wig and clothes, nice condition.                            Size 15"         $ 45-55
                                 Size 20-22"        50-60

```
1970 Price Comparison
Size 14-22"    $25
```

Illus. No. 13
"Effanbee Anne
Shirley" 21" tall

### (Walking Doll)

MAKERS: David S. Cohen & Joseph Lyon & Co. of N.Y., N.Y. Martin & Runyon of London, England and others.

DATE: 1862 - Patented by Enoch Rice Morrison, N.Y., N.Y.

MATERIAL: Heads made of pale bisque, china, cloth or papier-mâché. Under the skirt is the mechanism enclosed in a cardboard bell. The base of this bell is a circle of wood with slits where the metal feet protrude.

MARK: "Patented, July 15, 1862" found on underside of wooden circle.

SIZE: 10 inch

---

Marked Autoperipatetikos: Head of china, bisque, cloth or papier-mâché, leather arms, original clothes or nicely dressed. In fine working shape.     Size 10"   $600 and up*

* Not enough price samples to justify a reliable range

| 1970 |
| Price Comparison |
| Size 10"   $300 |

Illus. No. 14
Autoperipatetikos
10"

# BABY DAINTY
## (EFFanBEE)

MAKER: EFFanBEE Doll Corp., New York, N.Y., U.S.A.
   (Bernard Fleischaker and Hugo Baum)
DATE: Ca. 1912 - on
MATERIAL: Composition shoulder head, cloth body, composi-
   tion arms and legs; jointed at shoulders and hips.
MARK: "EFFANBEE
      BABY DAINTY"
SIZE: Various

---

Marked Baby Dainty: Composition shoulder head, painted molded
   hair, painted facial features, cloth stuffed body jointed at
   shoulders and hips, with curved arms and straight legs of
   composition. Original or good clothes; all in nice condition.

                          Size 15"        $ 25-35

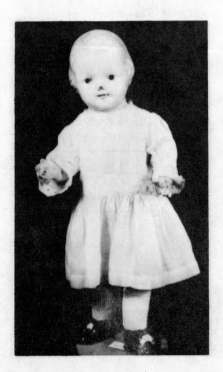

| 1970 Price Comparison |
| --- |
| Size 12-15"    $14 |

Illus. No. 15
"Effanbee
Baby Dainty"
14" tall

MAKER: Fleischaker & Baum, New York, N.Y., U.S.A.
DATE: 1914 - on
MATERIAL: Molded composition shoulder head and limbs, cloth
   body
MARK: "EFFanBEE Baby Grumpy"
SIZE: 11-1/2" and larger

---

*Marked "Baby Grumpy": Composition shoulder head with
   frowning face, molded and painted hair, painted eyes, closed
   mouth, composition arms and legs, cloth body, dressed;
   all in good condition.          Size 12"          $50-60
*A similar doll with grumpy expression is marked "Effanbee
   Dolls - Walk, Talk, Sleep" and has a deeper chest plate.
   Prices as above.

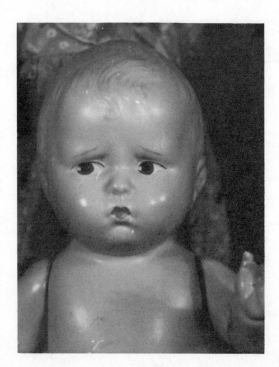

Illus. No. 15A
Grumpy-type
"Effanbee
Dolls-Walk, Talk,
Sleep" 12" tall.

# BABY SNOOKS
### (Ideal)

MAKER: Ideal Novelty & Toy Co., New York, N.Y., U.S.A.
DATE: 1938 - 1939
MATERIAL: Head, torso, hands and feet of composition; arms
    and legs made of flexible metal cable.
MARK: Round tag hanging on doll reads: "FLEXY -- an Ideal
    Doll, Fanny Brices Baby Snooks"
SIZE: 12-1/2"

---

Baby Snooks Doll: Doll described above complete with tag,
    dressed in original pajama-type suit; all in good condition.

Size 12-1/2"   $ 65-75

> 1970 Price Comparison
> Size 12-1/2"   $22

For picture see DOLLS, IMAGES OF LOVE by Madalaine
Selfridge, page 113

MAKER: Bähr & Pröschild
DATE: 1910 - on
MATERIAL: Bisque head, composition bent-limb baby or
    toddler body

MARK:         with "Germany" and
numbers 585, 604, 624

SIZE: Various

---

Marked B.P. Character: Bisque socket head, sleep eyes, open
  or open-closed mouth, good wig; composition bent-limb
  baby body; dressed; all in good condition.  10"-12"$225-275*
                                  15"-17"  250-295*

                                    *Allow extra for
                                    a toddler body

Illus. No. 16
"B & P
  585
Germany"
Open/closed
mouth 12"
tall

# BÉBÉ BRU
## (Composition Body)

MAKER: Bru Jne. & Cie., Paris, France
DATE: Ca. 1873 to 1899
MATERIAL: Bisque head, papier-mâché jointed body
MARK: "BRU", "BRU JNE", or "BÉBÉ BRU"; also,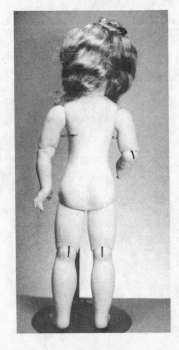
    are Bru marks
SIZE: Various

---

Marked Bru:Bisque head, closed mouth, beautiful paperweight
    eyes, lovely wig, pierced ears, good body, lovely clothes. All
    in nice condition. Size 20" $2,500 and up*
    *Not enough price samples to justify a reliable range.

| 1970 Price Comparison |
| --- |
| Size 11-22"    $950.00 |

Illus. No.17 & 18 "Bru Jeune #7
16-1/2". Front & back view.

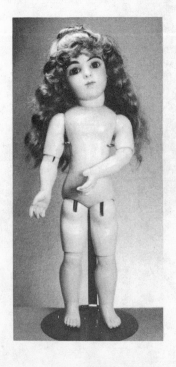

# BÉBÉ BRU
### (Kid Body)

MAKER: Bru Jne. & Cie., Paris, France
DATE: Ca. 1879 to 1899
MATERIAL: Bisque shoulder head, gusseted all-kid body,
 bisque hands
MARK: "BRU", "BRU JNE", "BÉBÉ BRU"; also
 are Bru marks
SIZE: Various

---

Marked Bébé Bru: Bisque swivel head on bisque shoulder plate,
 beautiful wig, set blown glass eyes, closed mouth, pierced
 ears, gusseted kid body, stitched toes, bisque hands and
 most of fore arm, lovely clothes. All in fine shape.

Size 20-24" $2500-3500
 28"      4000 up

1970 Price Comparison
Size 18-24"     $1350

Illus. No. 19
Marked "Bru Jne 7"
 23"

# BÉBÉ BRU
## (BÉBÉ TÉTEUR-Nursing)

MAKER: Bru Jne. & Cie., Paris, France
DATE: Ca. 1879 - 1899
MATERIAL: Bisque head, lower arms and hands, kid body.
Upper arm and upper legs of metal covered with kid. Lower
legs of carved wood.
MARK: "BRU", "BRU JNE", "BÉBÉ BRU" etc.
SIZE: Various

---

Marked Nursing Bru: Bisque head on shoulder plate, original or
lovely replacement wig, beautiful set eyes, open/closed
mouth with hole for nipple, kid body as above. Good clothing.
All in nice condition.                    Size 15" $1500-1800*
                                          *Not enough price
┌─────────────────────────────┐          samples to justify a
│ 1970 Price Comparison       │          reliable range.
│ Size 14-20"    $1295        │
└─────────────────────────────┘

Illus. No. 20
Bru Jne on head
Bru Jne also on left
shoulder
N.4T on right shoulder
14-1/2"

# BÉBÉ PHÉNIX

MAKER: Henri Alexandre, Paris France; Tourrel; Jules
    Steiner; Jules Mettais
DATE: 1889 - in 1895 the Bébé Phénix trademark was registered
    by Maison Jules Steiner.
MATERIAL: Bisque head, jointed papier-mâché body
MARK: BÉBÉ PHÉNIX        PHÉNIX-BABY
SIZE: Various
DESIGNER: Henri Alexandre

---

Marked Bébé Phénix: Beautiful bisque head, French jointed
  body, closed mouth, pierced ears, lovely old wig, bulbous
  set eyes, well dressed; all in fine condition. 20" $750-850*
Same as above with open mouth. Size 20" $550*

\*Not enough price samples
to justify a reliable range.

| 1970 Price Comparison |
| --- |
| Size 14-22"     $316 |

Illus. No. 21
"Modele
*92"
open mouth
20" tall
(Made by Mettais)

# BELTON-TYPE CHILD
## (So-called)

MAKER: Unknown
DATE: Ca.1880
MATERIAL: Bisque socket head, ball-jointed composition body
  with straight wrists
MARK: None
SIZE: Various

---

Belton-type Child Doll: Bisque socket head, solid but flat on top
  with 2 or 3 small holes, paperweight eyes, closed mouth,
  pierced ears; composition ball-jointed body with straight
  wrists; dressed; all in good condition. Size 15-17" $400-475
                                                   26"   600-675

Illus. No. 22
Unmarked-14-1/2"
tall.

MAKER: C. M. Bergmann of Waltershausen, Thüringia,
   Germany
DATE: Ca. 1897 - well into the 1900's
MATERIAL: Bisque head, composition ball-jointed body
MARK: "C. M. Bergmann - Germany" Sometimes with S & H
   (Simon & Halbig)
SIZE: Various

---

Bergmann Child Doll: Marked bisque head, composition ball-
   jointed body, sleep or set eyes, open mouth, good wig,
   dressed. All in nice condition.    Size 22-26"   $135-185
                                  29-31"    225-275

1970
Price Comparison
Size 21-30"  $90

Illus. No. 23
C. M. Bergmann
"Simon & Halbig
8-1/2"
22"

MAKER: Various German firms; few dolls are marked
DATE: Ca. 1890 to 1920
MATERIAL: Bisque heads, cloth bodies, china or bisque
    extremities
MARK: Some with numbers and/or "Germany"
SIZE: Various

---

Bonnet Doll: Bisque head with painted molded hair and molded
    fancy bonnet with bows, ribbons, flowers, feathers, etc.;
    original cloth body with original arms and legs, good old
    clothes or newly dressed; all in good condition.

| 1970 Price Comparison |
| :--- |
| Size 12-16"    $100 |

Size 12-16"   $150-200

Illus. No. 24
Bonnet Doll Shoulder Heads

MAKER: Various German and French doll makers from their
regular molds or specially designed ones with Negroid
features

DATE: 1890 - on

MATERIAL: Bisque socket heads either painted dark or with
dark coloring mixed in the slip of the bisque (this runs from
light brown to very dark) composition body in a matching
color

MARK: Various

SIZE: Various

---

Since these dolls are offered infrequently not enough price
samples have been found to justify a reliable range.

Size 14" Heubach Köppelsdorf Toddler     $ 250
11" AM 1894 (India Costume)              170
15" AM Dream Baby                        425

15" Tête Jumeau open
mouth$525

15" Steiner(French)open
mouth$750

14" A.M Rockabye Baby
$ 325

19" S&H Mulatto Girl   300
12" S&H 1078 Girl      285
21-1/2" Handwerck
109-11 Girl            350
14" Kestner Closed
Mouth Girl             950
11" K*R 126 Baby       325
15" K*R 100 Kaiser
Baby                   325

Illus. No. 25
"A.M. 351"
Black
Rockabye Baby
14" tall

MAKERS: Various
DATE: 1920 - on
MATERIAL: All-composition
MARK: Mostly unmarked
SIZE: Various

---

Negro all-composition: Bent-limb baby or toddler type, jointed
   at hips and shoulders and perhaps neck; molded hair,
   painted or sleep eyes, original clothes or good new ones.
   Some have three yarn tufts (on either side and on top.) All
   in good condition.                    Baby  Size 8-11" $20-35
                                   Toddler   16-18"   55-65

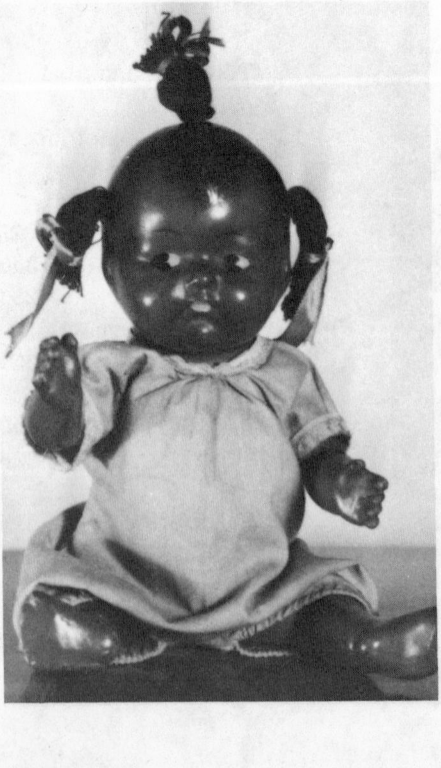

1970
Price Comparison
Size 10-16"    $13

Illus. No. 26
Black Baby
"G E W"
9" tall

# BLOND BISQUE CHILD
## (So-called American School Boy)

MAKER: Unknown German firms
DATE: Ca. 1870's into 1890's
MATERIAL: Bisque shoulder head, kid or cloth (or combination) body
MARK: Some with numbers and/or "Germany"
SIZE: Various

---

Molded Hair Child:Blond bisque shoulder head, molded hair, glass eyes, kid or cloth body, good bisque or kid arms, closed mouth, nicely dressed; all in good condition.
Size 11-14" $250-350

| 1970 |
| Price Comparison |
| 10-13"        $85 |
| Blue or Brown |
| Set Eyes |
| 12-18"       $135 |

Illus. No. 27
"Germany &
30/B2"   15"

# BONNIE BABE
## (Georgene Averill Baby)

MAKER: Heads by Alt, Beck & Gottschalck of Nauendorf, Thüringia, Germany. Cloth bodies by George Borgfeldt & Co. of New York, N.Y.

DATE: 1926, renewed 1946

MATERIAL: Bisque heads, cloth bodies, composition arms and legs

MARK: "Georgene Averill"

SIZE: Various

DESIGNER: Georgene Averill, U.S.A.

---

Marked Bonnie Babe: Bisque head, cloth body, composition extremities, molded hair, set or sleep eyes, open mouth with two teeth, dressed, all in good condition.

| 1970 Price Comparison Size 15-23"    $229 |
|---|

Size 16-18"   $650-675
21-22"    725-775

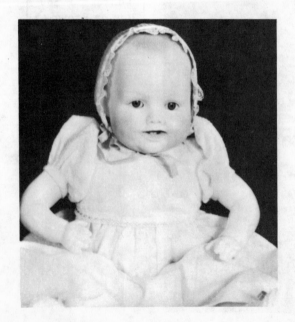

Illus. No. 28
Georgene
Averill
Bonnie Babe
16" tall

MAKERS: Various French, U.S. and Italian firms
DATE: Early 1920's into the early 1930's
MATERIAL: Heads of composition and other materials, bodies
    mostly cloth but also of composition and other substances.
MARK: Mostly unmarked
SIZE: Many 24" to 36". Some smaller

---

Boudoir Doll:Composition shoulder head, painted features;
    composition or cloth stuffed body;unusually long extremities;
    usually high-heeled shoes;original clothes-elaborately de-
    signed and trimmed. All in good condition. Size 24-28"
    $20-30.

1970
Price
Comparison
Size 24-36"
$22

Illus. No. 29
Boudoir Doll
24 inches

# BUBBLES
### (EFFanBEE)

MAKER: EFFanBEE Doll Corporation (Fleischaker & Baum)
　　New York, N.Y., U.S.A.
DATE: 1924 - on
MATERIAL: Composition head and arms, cloth body, cloth or
　　composition legs
MARK: "EFFanBEE BUBBLES 1924" or "EFFanBEE DOLLS
　　WALK, TALK, SLEEP.  Made in U.S.A." also a tag on
　　wrist printed "This is BUBBLES"
SIZE: Various

---

Marked Bubbles: Composition head with blond molded painted
　　hair. Cloth body, curved composition arms and legs,
　　original clothes, open mouth, sleep eyes. All in good shape.

Size 20-25"　　$50-60*
　　14-15"　　30-40*
*Allow extra for
　　straight legs

1970 Price Comparison
Size 17-26"　　$ 35

Illus. No. 32
EFFanBEE Bubbles
19 © 24
13" Seated

MAKER: Name of maker kept secret by H. D. Lee Co., Inc.
  Garment Manufacturers of Kansas City, Missouri, for whom
  dolls were made.
DATE: 1920 to 1962
MATERIAL: Composition from 1920 to 1948. Hard plastic from
  1949 until 1962.
MARK: "BUDDY LEE" embossed across shoulders
SIZE: 13 inch only

---

Marked Buddy Lee: Early all-composition; molded, painted
  eyes and hair; jointed only at shoulders - legs apart;
  dressed in original Lee clothes. Eyes to side; all in good
  shape.                           Size 13"        $ 65-75
Marked Buddy Lee: Later all hard plastic doll. Mold changed
  slightly by slimming the legs - making the doll easier to
  dress and undress. This was done in 1949. Molded painted
  hair, painted eyes to side; jointed at shoulders; legs apart;
  dressed in Lee original clothes; all in nice condition.
                                   Size 13"        $ 50-55

| 1970 Price Comparison |
| Size 13" Composition |
| $ 45 |
| Size 13" Plastic 22 |

Illus. No. 31
Buddy Lee - All original
Plastic - 13"

# BYE-LO BABY
## (Bisque Head)

MAKER: Heads - J.D. Kestner of Waltershausen, Thüringia, Germany. Alt, Beck & Gottschalck of Nauendorf, Thüringia. C. F. Kling & Co. of Ohrdruf, Thüringia. Hertel, Schwab & Co. of Luisenthal near Ohrdruf, Thüringia. Bodies - K & K Toy Co. of New York, N.Y.

DATE: 1923 - on

MATERIAL: Bisque head, cloth body, celluloid or composition hands

MARK: "BYE-LO BABY" on body, "GRACE STOREY PUTNAM" on head - some dated 1923

SIZE: Seven sizes, from 9" to 20"

DESIGNER: Grace Storey Putnam (both head and body), U.S.A.

---

Marked Bye-Lo Baby: Fine condition, bisque head, cloth body, sleep eyes, dressed.

| | Head Size | |
|---|---|---|
| | 8-11" | $ 200-300 |
| | 12-16" | 325-450 |

| 1970 |  |
|---|---|
| Price Comparison | |
| 15-20" | $ 150 |
| 9-13" | 121 |

Illus. No. 33
Marked Bye-Lo Baby
Bisque Head

**(Composition Head)**

MAKER: Cameo Doll Co., New York, N.Y. (Composition heads
  only)
DATE: 1924 - on
MATERIAL: Composition head, cloth body
MARK: "GRACE STOREY PUTNAM"
SIZE: Various
DESIGNER: Grace Storey Putnam, U.S.A.

---

Marked BYE-LO BABY: Composition head, cloth body, sleep
  eyes, composition hands, nice clothes.

Head Size  10-12-1/2"  $85-100

> 1970 Price Comparison
> Size 12-15"      $ 75

For picture see:  TWENTIETH CENTURY DOLLS: From Bisque
  to Vinyl  by Johanna Anderton, page 116, photo BLB-2.

**CAMPBELL KID**
(Horsman)

MAKER: E. I. Horsman Co., Inc., New York, N.Y., U.S.A.
DATE: 1910 to 1914
MATERIAL: Composition head and arms, cloth body and legs
MARK: "E.I.H. ©1910"
SIZE: Various

---

Campbell Kid: Marked composition head with flange neck,
   original cloth body, composition arms, cloth legs and feet,
   original romper suit, all in nice condition.   Size 12" $55-75

| 1970 Price Comparison |
| :--- |
| Size 9-15"        $ 21 |

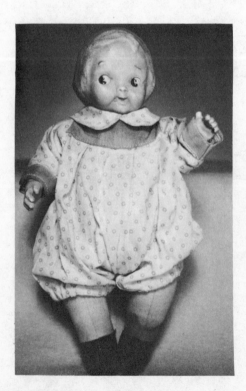

Illus. No. 33
Campbell Kid
(Original Suit)
Marked "E.I.H. ©1910"
                9"

MAKERS: Rheinische Gummi und Celluloid Fabrik Co.,
    Mannheim-Neckarau, Bavaria, Germany
DATE: These dolls from 1899 to perhaps the 1920's or later
MATERIAL: All celluloid
MARK: Embossed turtle mark with or without the diamond
    frame; sometimes "SCHUTZ MARKE" and "Made in
    Germany"
SIZE: Various

---

All celluloid Marked: Bent-limb baby or toddler, painted or
    glass set eyes, molded hair, jointed arms and/or legs,
    closed mouth, no clothes; all in good condition.

| | |
|---|---|
| Size 4-1/2-6" | $ 15-25 |
| 10-15" | 30-40 |
| 18" | 50-60 |

1970 Price Comparison
Size 7-18"        $ 26

Illus. No. 34
Turtle Mark in
Diamond on neck.
29 Underneath
    11"

**CELLULOID DOLLS**
(Kid, Cloth or Composition Body)

MAKERS: Rheinische Gummi und Celluloid Fabrik Co.,
    Mannheim-Neckarau, Bavaria, Germany
DATE: 1869 - on
MATERIAL: Celluloid head; jointed kid, cloth or composition
    body
MARK: Embossed turtle mark with or without the diamond
    frame; sometimes "SCHUTZ MARKE" and "Made in
    Germany". Also made celluloid heads from molds of
    Kestner and Kammer & Reinhart whose marks also appear
    on the heads.
SIZE: Various

---

Marked Celluloid Head: Celluloid shoulder head, painted hair
    and features, or glass eyes (set) and wig; open or closed
    mouth, celluloid or composition arms, dressed; all in good
    condition. On a cloth body. Size 12-14"  $40-60
    With glass eyes & wig, on a kid body. Size 17-23" $85-125
Celluloid socket head, glass eyes(sometimes flirty) and wig,
    open mouth, composition body (ball-jointed or bent-limb);
    dressed; all in good condition.    Size 14-16"    $95-135*
    Size 20-21"    $135-175*
    *Allow extra for flirty
    eyes.

1970 Price Comparison
Celluloid Shoulder
Head
Size 9-21" $36

Illus. No. 35 Turtle & Mark
"Made in Germany"
Flirty-eyes
14-1/2 inches tall.

MAKER: Century Doll Co., New York, N.Y. Bisque heads by
    J.D. Kestner, Germany
DATE: Ca. 1925
MATERIAL: Bisque head, cloth body, composition arms (and
    legs)
MARK: "Century Doll Co."    Sometimes  ⟨K⟩  or Kestner
       "Germany"
SIZE: Various

---

Marked Century Infant: Bisque solid dome head, molded and
    painted sleep eyes, closed or open-closed mouth, cloth body,
    composition hands or limbs, dressed; all in good condition.

                               Size 12-15"    $200-250

      Illus. No. 36
    "Century Doll Co.
  Kestner-Germany 11"
      seated.

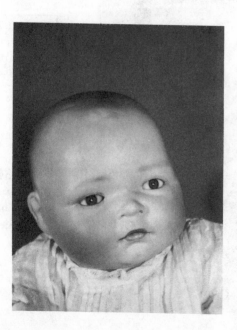

# CHARLIE McCARTHY
## (EFFanBEE)

MAKER: EFFanBEE Doll Corp. (Fleischaker & Baum), New
York, N.Y., U.S.A.
DATE: 1937 - on
MATERIAL: Composition head, cloth body
MARK: "EDGAR BERGEN'S CHARLIE McCARTHY, an
EFFanBEE PRODUCT"
SIZE: Various

---

Marked Charlie McCarthy: Composition head, cloth body,
strings at back of head to open and close mouth; painted hair
and eyes, original clothes, all in good condition.

| | |
|---|---|
| Size 20" | $50 |
| Size 30" | $75 |

1970
Price
Comparison
Size 20-30"  $30

Illus. No. 37
Charlie McCarthy
Unmarked
39 inches tall.

MAKER: Martha Jenks Chase, Pawtucket, Rhode Island, U.S.A.
DATE: 1891 to ca. 1951 - (play doll)
MATERIAL: Stockinet and cloth
MARK: "Chase Stockinet Doll" on left leg or under left arm,
    paper label on back (Usually gone)
SIZE: 9" to life size
DESIGNER: Martha Jenks Chase

---

Marked Chase Doll in good condition, dressed. Size 18-26"
    $100-175*. *Allow extra for rare bobbed hair with bangs.

| 1970 Price Comparison | |
|---|---|
| Size 16-25" | $ 62 |

Illus.No.38:Left photo:Chase Baby
Marked on Doll's Left Upper
Thigh in front. 12-1/2 inches.
Illus.No.39:Right photo:Unusual
Paper Label on back of same doll.

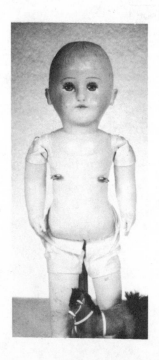
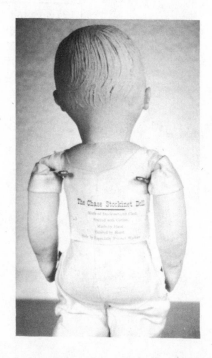

# CHILD DOLL
### (Amberg)

MAKER: Louis Amberg & Son, New York, N.Y., U.S.A.
DATE: Ca. 1928
MATERIAL: All composition, jointed at waist, shoulders and
    hips
MARK: "Amberg Pat. pen. L.A. & Son, 1928"
SIZE: Various

---

Amberg Child Doll: Marked all composition doll; jointed at
    waist, hips and shoulders; painted facial features, molded
    hair, closed mouth, original clothes; all in nice condition.

                          Size 12-14"     $65

| 1970 Price Comparison |
| :--- |
| Size 12-16"    $33 |

For photograph see WENDY & FRIENDS by Madalaine
    Selfridge, page 86.

MAKER: Francis H. Bawo & Charles T. Dotter, Bavaria; New
York, N.Y., U.S.A.; Limoges, France; Carlsbad, Austria
DATE: 1880
MATERIAL: China shoulder head, cloth body with printed
corset
MARK: "Pat. Dec. 7/80" on back of shoulder
SIZE: Various
DESIGNER: Charles T. Dotter

---

Marked "Dotter" China Head: Cloth body, old or new china arms,
sewn on kid boots, nicely costumed; all in good condition.

| 1970 Price Comparison |
| --- |
| Size 16-24"      $133 |

Size 13-16"     $110-125
18-20"     125-150

Illus. No. 40
Size "4-Pat. Dec. 7/80"
18 inches

**CHINA HEAD DOLL—"Bald"**
(Biedermeier-So-called)

MAKER: Unknown German firms
DATE: 1840's thru the early 1900's
MATERIAL: Bald china shoulder head, some with black areas on
    top of head; cloth body, bisque, china or leather arms.
MARK: None
SIZE: Various

---

"BALD" China Doll: China shoulder head, blue painted eyes,
    proper wig, kid arms, old cloth body, nice dress; all in
    good condition.                    Size 14-18"    $350-400

> 1970 Price Comparison
> Size 13-20"        $235

Illus. No. 41: Left Photo
"Bald" China Head
Original Clothes  16"

Illus. No. 42: Right Photo
Same doll with wig

MAKER: Unknown German firms
DATE: 1880's thru 1890's
MATERIAL: China shoulder head on cloth or kid body
MARK: Some marked "Germany"
SIZE: Various

---

"BANG" China Doll: Black or blond-haired china shoulder head, bangs on forehead, original cloth or kid body, leather arms, blue painted eyes, old china legs, dressed; all in good condition.                              Size 19-22"   $150-195

| 1970 Price Comparison |
| --- |
| Size 14-25"      $ 84 |

Illus. No. 43

Two "Bang" China Heads  Black 15"   Blond 18"

**CHINA HEAD DOLL—"COMMON"**
### (Also Called Low Brow)

MAKER: Unknown German firms
DATE: 1880's to 1940
MATERIAL: China shoulder head, cloth or kid body; stub,
    leather, bisque or china limbs.
MARK: Some with numbers and/or "Germany"
SIZE: Various

---

"COMMON" China Head Doll: Black or blond wavy hair style as
    pictured; blue painted eyes, old body, old limbs, original or
    good clothes; all in good condition.  Size 7"    $   37.50

                                    14-16"    80-90

| 1970 Price Comparison | 20-22"   100-125* |
|---|---|
| 16-27" $65;  6-14" $29 | *Prices include <u>old</u> |

                                      body & limbs

Illus. No. 44 Two "Common"
China Heads  20" & 12"

Illus. No. 45
"Common" China Head
Blond 20"

MAKER: Unknown German firms
DATE: 1840 to 1870
MATERIAL: China shoulder head, cloth body, varied extremities
MARK: None
SIZE: Various

---

"COVERED WAGON" Doll: Black-haired china shoulder head, pink tint, blue painted eyes, old cloth body, arms and legs; very well dressed; all in good condition.   14-18" $250-275

> 1970 Price Comparison
> Size 16-28"  $83
> With brown eyes-Size 18-29"  $225

Illus. No. 46
"Covered Wagon" China
Head    23"

MAKER: Unknown German firms
DATE: 1875 to 1895
MATERIAL: China shoulder head, cloth body, leather arms
MARK: None
SIZE: Various

---

"Dolley Madison" China Doll: Black-haired china shoulder head,
   molded ribbon bow in front and molded band on back of head;
   painted blue eyes, beautiful clothes, original cloth body,
   leather arms and boots; entire doll in fine condition.

| 1970 Price Comparison |
| --- |
| Size 14-29"      $179 |

Size 15-20"    $150-200

Illus. No. 47
"Dolley Madison"
China Head Doll  16"

MAKER: Unknown German firms
DATE: Late 1850 thru late 1870
MATERIAL: China shoulder head, cloth body; extremities
    leather or china
MARK: None
SIZE: Various

---

"FLAT TOP" China Doll: China shoulder head with black hair,
    old cloth body, painted blue eyes, leather arms and boots or
    china limbs, old clothes or newly well costumed; all in good
    condition. Size 9-12" $75- 85*
Size 15-16" $90-95;Size 18-21"
$145-185;Size 22-26" $185-225.
*Allow extra for brown eyes.

| 1970 Price Comparison | |
|---|---|
| Size 7-13" | $53 |
| Size 15-27" | $74-95 |

Illus. No. 48. Left Photo:"Flat Top"China Head 19 inches.
Illus. No. 49. Right Photo: "Flat Top" Chinas 14" and 18"

**CHINA HEAD DOLL—"K" in BELL**
(Kling & Co.)

MAKER: Kling & Co. of Ohrdruf, Thüringia, Germany
DATE: 1880's to 1900
MATERIAL: China shoulder head, cloth body, bisque or china
limbs

MARK: and sometimes "Germany"

SIZE: Various

---

Marked "Kling" China Doll: Pink tinted black or blond-haired
china head, old cloth body, original arms and legs; lovely
costume; all in good condition.    Size 18-20"   $160 and up*
*Not enough price
samples to justify a
reliable range

1970 Price Comparison
Size 12"-14"  $65

Illus. No. 50
Marked "Kling" China
Head   10-1/2"

MAKER: Hertwig & Co. of Katzhütte, Thüringia; and/or Closter
    Veilsdorf, Thüringia, Germany
DATE: 1905 - on
MATERIAL: China shoulder head, cloth body - some with
    printed alphabet or other figures printed on cotton material;
    china limbs
MARK: Some with "Germany"
SIZE: Various
NAMES: "AGNES", "BERTHA", "DAISY", "DOROTHY",
    "EDITH", "ESTHER", "ETHEL","FLORENCE", "HELEN",
    "MABEL","MARION", "PAULINE", ETC.

---

"Pet Name" China Doll: China shoulder head, molded yoke with
    name, black or blond painted hair (one-third were blond);
    painted blue eyes; old cloth body, good old limbs, dressed
    properly; all in good condition.    Size 15-20" $ 70-100*
                                  24-27"   150-200*
                        *Do not pay as much
                            for new body and
                            limbs.

| 1970 Price Comparison |
| --- |
| Size 8-18"     $ 54 |
| 19-28"       82 |

Illus. No. 51
Bertha 10" Name China
"Patent applied for
Germany"
Ethel 18"

MAKER: Unknown German firms
DATE: 1860's and 1870's
MATERIAL: China shoulder head with molded snood in hair;
  cloth or kid body, limbs varied but often of leather
MARK: None
SIZE: Various

---

"SNOOD" China Head Doll: Black painted hair, slender features,
  painted blue eyes, molded eyelids, gold colored snood, deep
  shoulders, 3 sew holes, cloth body with old china arms;
  beautifully gowned; all in nice condition.   17-20" $350-500*

1970 Price Comparison
Size 17-20"      $293

*Not enough price samples
to justify a reliable range.

*China heads with unusual
hair styles and features are
the most desired by collectors; hence the most difficult
to find.

Illus. No. 52
China Head with gold band
and gold snood enclosing
lower half of molded hair 12"

MAKER: Cuno & Otto Dressel of Sonneberg, Thüringia, Germany
DATE: Ca. 1900
MATERIAL: Bisque shoulder head, jointed kid or cloth body;
   bisque socket head, ball-jointed composition body.
MARK: "C & O Dressel - Germany", "C O D", etc.
SIZE: Various

---

C O D DOLL: Marked bisque head, original jointed kid or
   composition body, good wig, glass eyes, open mouth,
   suitable clothes; all in good condition.    12-15" $ 85-100
   
   19-22"  125-150
   
   25"    175

> 1970 Price Comparison
> Size 13-19"    $67

Illus. No. 53
"COD 23-5DEP"
Shoulder Head-
Kid Body
20-1/2"

# DEANNA DURBIN
## (Ideal)

MAKER: Ideal Novelty & Toy Co., Brooklyn, N.Y., U.S.A.
DATE: 1938
MATERIAL: Composition
MARK: "DEANNA DURBIN, IDEAL DOLL, U.S.A."
SIZE: Various

---

Marked Deanna Durbin: All-composition doll, jointed at neck,
shoulders and hips; sleep eyes, smiling mouth with teeth.
Original wig, original clothing. All in nice condition.

| 1970 Price Comparison |
|---|
| Size 18-24"     $45 |

Size 21"  $125*
*Allow extra for button

Illus. No. 54
Deanna Durbin, Ideal
Doll, U.S.A. 21"

MAKER: Alexander Doll Co., New York, N.Y., U.S.A.
DATE: Dec. 1935
MATERIAL: Composition; toddler or bent-limb bodies
MARK: "ALEXANDER"
SIZE: 7-1/2" to 20"
DESIGNER: Bernard Lipfert

---

Marked Quintuplet: All composition with original clothing,
toddler or bent-limb bodies, nice condition.

| 1970 Price Comparison |
| --- |
| Size 6-9" each $33 |
| 14-23" each un- |
| dressed $35 |

Size 7-1/2" each $35-45
14-17"   each   60-75
10-11"   each   45-55

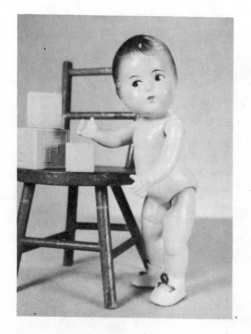

Illus. No. 55
"Alexander" embossed
on back of head and
across shoulders
7-1/2"

MAKER: Various German firms
DATE: Ca. 1890 to 1920
MATERIAL: Bisque head, molded hair or wigged; cloth body,
    bisque arms and legs
MARK: Sometimes "Germany"
SIZE: Various small sizes

---

Doll House Doll: Man or lady 4-1/2" to 6", as above with
    painted eyes, original clothes or suitably dressed; all in
    nice condition.                    Sizes 4-1/2-6"  $80-100*

*This price includes only dolls of very good quality with
old bodies and limbs.

> 1970 Price Comparison
> Sizes 4-1/2-6"  $30

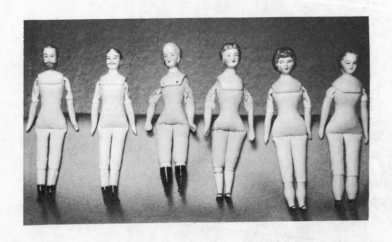

Illus. No. 56 Types of doll house dolls listed above.

# E. D. BÉBÉ

MAKER: Unknown as yet but <u>possibly</u> by E. Denamur of Paris,
  France
DATE: Ca. 1885 into 1890's
MATERIAL: Bisque head, papier-mâché jointed body
MARK: "E D", and sometimes a number
SIZE: Various

---

Marked E. D. BÉBÉ: Bisque head, papier-mâché jointed body,
  good wig, closed mouth, pierced ears, beautiful blown
  glass eyes, nicely dressed, good condition.

15-1/2"-21"  $500-695

Same as above, but with open mouth. Size 20-26" $400-500

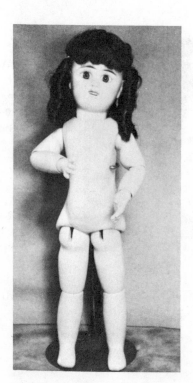

```
1970
Price Comparison
Size 12-20"$286
With Open Mouth
Size 12-20"$132
```

Illus. No. 57 E 5 D
Deposé 15"

# EDEN BÉBÉ

MAKER: Fleischmann & Bloedel of Fürth, Bavaria and Paris, France

DATE: Founded in Bavaria in 1873. Also in Paris by 1890, then on into S.F.B.J. in 1899

MATERIAL: Bisque head, papier-mâché body

MARK: "EDEN BÉBÉ, PARIS"

SIZE: Various

---

Marked Eden Bébé: Bisque head, jointed papier-mâché body with unjointed wrists, beautiful wig, large set paperweight eyes, pierced ears, lovely clothes, closed or open/closed mouth, all in nice condition.    Size 13-15" $475-550

Same as above with open mouth.    Size 17-20" $425-495

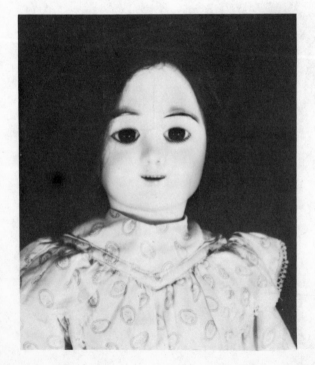

1970
Price
Comparison
Size 20-25"
$285

Illus. No. 58
"Eden Bébé
Paris
9
Deposé"
22" tall

MAKER: Co-operative Manufacturing Co., Springfield, Vt., U.S.A.

DATE: 1873

MATERIAL: Composition head, fully jointed wooden body. Metal feet and wooden or metal hands.

MARK: None - unless black paper band around waist still exists with patent date printed on it.

SIZE: 12" to 18"

---

Joel Ellis Wooden Doll: Composition head (over wood). Painted brown eyes, jointed wooden body (mortise-and-tenon), molded hair, metal hands and feet. Nicely dressed in old clothes. All in only fair shape.     (depending on condition)
Size 15"  $250-550

1970
Price  Comparison
Size 12"-15"$150

Illus. No. 59 Joel Ellis
12-1/2"

# F. G. BÉBÉ

MAKER: F. Gaultier, Paris (1860) later Gaultier and Fils, St. Maurice, Charenton, Seine, Paris, France
DATE: 1879 to 1900 and probably later
MATERIAL: Bisque head, jointed papier-mâché body
MARK: "F.G." or "F. G." in a scroll
SIZE: Various

---

Marked F.G. Bébé: Bisque head, papier-mâché body, good French wig, closed mouth, beautiful large set eyes, pierced ears, well dressed; all in nice condition. 17-19"$700-800

Same as above with open mouth. Size 17-19" $395

| 1970 Price Comparison |
| --- |
| Size 9-10" $150 |
| Size 14-20"$330 |

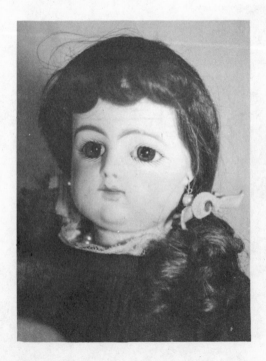

Illus. No. 60 Marked
"F.G." 15"

### (So-called)

MAKER: Gaultier, A., Paris, (1860) later F. Gaultier and Fils,
St. Maurice, Charenton, Seine and Paris, France.
DATE: Late 1860's to ca. 1910
MATERIAL: Bisque head, kid body
MARK: "F. G." or "F.G." in a scroll
SIZE: Various

---

Marked F.G. French Fashion: Bisque swivel head on bisque
shoulder plate, original kid body, kid arms with wired
fingers or bisque lower arms and hands; original or good
French wig, lovely large stationary eyes, original or good
clothes, closed mouth, ears pierced; all in nice condition.

Size 15-17" $450-575
Size 24-25" $900-950

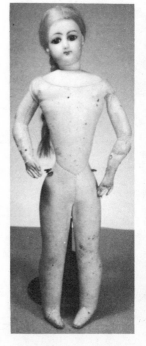 

1970
Price
Comparison
10-14"$203
15-18"$327

Illus. No. 61
Marked "F.G."
12 inch.

Illus. No. 62
Back View of
Same Doll

# FLORA McFLIMSEY
## (Mme. Alexander)

MAKER: Alexander Doll Co., New York, N.Y., U.S.A.
DATE: 1938
MATERIAL: All composition
MARK: Head: "Princess Elizabeth
Alexander Doll Co."
Dress tag: "Flora McFlimsey
of Madison Square
by Madame Alexander, N.Y."
SIZE:

---

Marked Flora McFlimsey: All composition, sleep eyes, open
mouth, freckles on nose, human hair wig of red-brown,
original clothes; all in good condition. Size 14" $50-60*

*Not enough
price samples
to justify a
reliable range.

Illus. No. 63
"Flora
McFlimsey"
Marked as
above
14-1/2"tall

ORIGINATOR: George Borgfeldt & Co. of New York, N.Y.,
    U.S.A.
MAKER: Armand Marseille of Köppelsdorf, Thüringia, Germany
DATE: 1901
MATERIAL: Bisque head, composition ball-jointed body
MARK: "Florodora A.M. Made in Germany"
SIZE: Various

---

Marked Florodora: Bisque head, composition ball-jointed body,
    open mouth, sleep eyes, good wig, well dressed, all in
    nice condition.
        Size 15–19"   $90–135
        Size 22–26"   $145–175

> 1970 Price Comparison
>   Size 12–18" $47
>   Size 20–28" $70

Illus.No.64 Florodora
Ball-jointed body
"A 3/0 xm
Made in Germany"
14-1/2 inch

# FLORODORA—KID BODY
## (A.M.)

ORIGINATOR: George Borgfeldt & Co., of New York, N.Y., U.S.A.
MAKER: Armand Marseille of Köppelsdorf, Thüringia, Germany
DATE: 1901
MATERIAL: Bisque shoulder head, jointed kid body
MARK: "FLORODORA A.M. MADE IN GERMANY"
SIZE: Various

---

Marked Florodora: Bisque head, kid body, bisque hands, open
   mouth, good wig, sleep eyes, nicely dressed; all in good
   condition.                          Size 14-19"   $ 85-125
                                       Size 23-25"   $135-185

```
1970 Price Comparison
  Size 12-23" $54
```

Illus.No.65 Florodora
Kid Body
"A.M. 3/0 DRGM
Made in Germany"
17-1/2 inch

# FRENCH BÉBÉ
### (Unmarked)

MAKERS: Numerous French firms
DATE: Ca. 1860 to ca. 1925
MATERIAL: Bisque head, jointed papier-mâché body
MARK: None except perhaps numbers, Paris, or France
SIZE: Various

---

Unmarked French BÉBÉ: Beautiful bisque head, swivel neck,
 set paperweight eyes, ears pierced, closed mouth, lovely
 wig, solid or open crown, jointed French body, pretty
 costume; all in good condition.   Size 17-18"   $550-650
Same as above except with open mouth.   Size 14-22"   $275-385

1970
Price
Comparison
10-1/2-16"
$267
Open Mouth
13-21"$154

Illus. No. 66
French Bébé
Unmarked
17 inch.

# FRENCH FASHION-UNMARKED
### (So-called)

MAKER: Various French firms
DATE: Ca. 1860 through 1890's
MATERIAL: Bisque shoulder head; jointed kid body; some all-
    wood jointed
MARK: None, except possibly numbers or letters
SIZE: Various

---

French Fashion: Unmarked bisque shoulder head, swivel neck,
    kid body, kid arms--some with wired fingers; or old bisque
    arms; original or good wig; lovely blown glass eyes, closed
    mouth, earrings; original or other fine clothes; all in very
    nice condition.         Size 11-18"  $400-575
                                 Size 24-28"  $695-950

1970
Price Comparison
Size 11-15"$292
Size 16-22"$333
Painted Eyes &
Stationary Neck
Size 11-18"$343

Illus. No. 67 Un-
marked French
Fashion Original
clothes 15 inch.

MAKERS: Various German firms
DATE: Ca. 1850's thru early 1900's
MATERIAL: Glazed china
MARK: None, except for "Germany", or numbers or both
SIZE: Various

---

Frozen Charlotte: All-china doll, simple hairdo - black molded, parted down the middle. Hands extended, legs separated but not jointed. No clothes; perfect condition.

size 2-4"    $25-45
size   5"      $50
size 13-15"   $400

1970 Price Comparison
Size 2-6"     $22

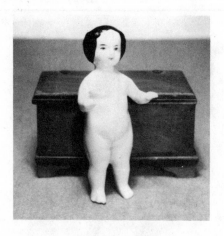

Illus. No. 68 Frozen Charlotte
3-1/2"

MAKER: Fulper Pottery Co. of Flemington, New Jersey, U.S.A.
DATE: 1918 to 1921
MATERIAL: Bisque heads only by Fulper; used on bodies made
by others

MARK: "Fulper -- Made in U.S.A." and others

SIZE: Various

---

Fulper Child Doll: Marked bisque head, good wig; kid jointed or
composition ball-jointed body; lovely set or sleep eyes, open
or closed mouth; suitably dressed. All in nice condition.
Size 19-25" $190-225.
Fulper Baby or Toddler: Same as above but with bent-limb or
jointed toddler body. Size 18-22" $225-300

> 1970 Price Comparison: Child Doll 16-20" $95
> Baby Doll 22-27" $84

Illus.No.69
Marked
Fulper-
Toddler
Type
19-1/2"
Doll in
Arms--a
Norah
Wellings
8 inch.

Illus.No.70
Marked
Fulper
15-1/2"
"EIH" on
body.

MAKER: Freundlich Novelty Corp. of New York, N.Y., U.S.A.
DATE: Ca. early 1940's
MATERIAL: All composition, molded hat, jointed at shoulders
    and hips.
MARK: Tag with "General MacArthur" and manufacturer's
    name and address etc.
SIZE: 18 inch

---

General MacArthur: All composition, molded hat, painted
    features. One arm made to salute if desired. Original
    khaki uniform with tags; jointed at shoulders and hips; all in
    good condition.                 Size 18"  $90-95.

> 1970
> Price Comparison
> Size 18"  $36

Illus. No. 71 General
Douglas MacArthur
18 inch.

**GERMAN BISQUE CHARACTER BABY**
(Bent-limb, Unmarked)

MAKER: Various German firms
DATE: 1910 - on
MATERIAL: Bisque head, composition bent-limb body
MARK: Some numbered, some "Germany", some both
SIZE: Various

---

Baby Doll: Bisque head, good wig, composition bent-limb body;
sleep eyes, open mouth, suitably dressed; all in fine
condition.     Size  7- 9"  $ 75- 95
                         Size 10-12"  $100-150
                         Size 14-18"  $165-195

Illus. No.72 Marked "Germany" Bisque Baby 14-1/2"tall.

### (Ball-jointed, Unmarked)

MAKER: Various German firms
DATE: Late 1880's to ca. 1940
MATERIAL: Bisque head, composition ball-jointed body
MARK: Only "Germany", numbers or both
SIZE: Various

---

Unmarked Child Doll: Bisque head marked "Germany", ball-
jointed composition body, good wig, open mouth, sleep eyes,
pretty clothes; all in nice condition.   Size 15-18"   $ 85-100
                                          Size 19-24"   $105-135

| 1970 Price Comparison | |
|---|---|
| Size 14-18" | $ 57 |
| Size 20-24" | $ 64 |

Illus. No. 73
Unmarked German
Bisque-Body
Marked "Germany"
22-1/2"
Doll in Arms
A.M. 1900
(original clothes)
8-1/2"

# GERMAN BISQUE HEAD
### (Closed mouth)

MAKERS: Various German firms
DATE: Ca. 1880 to ca. 1890
MATERIAL: Bisque shoulder heads; kid or cloth bodies, bisque
   hands. Bisque socket head; composition ball-jointed body
MARK: None except numbers and "Germany"
SIZE: Various

---

Unmarked Closed Mouth Doll: Bisque shoulder head, kid or
   cloth body, stitch jointed at shoulders, hips and knees; good
   bisque hands, nicely dressed; mohair wig; all in good
   condition. Size 11-12"   $175-250
                Size 14-20"     $295
                Size 22-24"     $350
Same as above, but with swivel neck: Size 20-23"   $325-350
Same as above, but with bald head. Size 14-23"   $325-395
Bisque socket head on composition body. 14-18"   $400-435

1970
Price Comparison
Size 7-11"  $38

Illus. No. 74 Unmarked
German Bisque
Shoulder Head--Kid
Body. 21"Tall.

MAKER: Various German firms
DATE: 1890 to World War I
MATERIAL: Bisque shoulder head, jointed kid body; bisque
 lower arms
MARK: Heads incised: "Mabel", "Darling", "Ruth", etc., with
 numbers and sometimes "Germany"
SIZE: Various

---

Name Shoulder Head: Bisque shoulder head marked with doll's
 name; jointed kid or cloth body, bisque lower arms, well
 dressed, set eyes, open mouth, good wig; all in fine condition.

| | |
|---|---|
| Size 11-13" | $ 60- 90 |
| Size 16-19" | $110-145 |
| Size 20-24" | $145-175 |

```
1970
Price Comparison
Size 16-27" $63
```

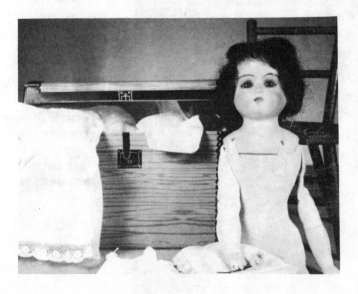

Illus. No. 75 "Ruth" name shoulder head in script and "18/0"11"

**GERMAN BISQUE SHOULDER HEAD**
**(Unmarked)**

MAKER: Various German firms
DATE: Ca. 1880 to 1920
MATERIAL: Bisque shoulder head, kid or cloth body (or
    combination). Bisque lower arms.
MARK: Some with numbers and/or "Germany"
SIZE: Various

---

Bisque Shoulder Head: Slightly turned bisque head, kid or cloth
    body. Original or good wig, open mouth, set or sleep eyes,
    good bisque lower arms, well dressed. All in nice condition.

| 1970 Price Comparison |
| With Open Mouth |
| Size 14-23"    $70 |

Size 13-16"    $ 75-100
Size 20-22"    $125-165

Illus. No. 76
Unmarked
German Bisque
Shoulder Head
incised
"278 Dep 8" Kid
Body 21"Tall

MAKER: Various German firms
DATE: Late 1880's to ca. 1940
MATERIAL: Bisque head, jointed composition body
MARK: None except numbers, "Germany" or both
SIZE: Up to 12"

---

Tiny Child Doll:Bisque socket head,composition five-piece body, good wig, open mouth, set or sleep eyes, cute clothes;all in nice condition. Size 5- 7"  $35-60*
Size 8-11"  $40-85*

*Higher price is for a ball-jointed body.

1970 Price Comparison
Size 5-10"    $34

Illus. No. 77 "Made in Germany" Otherwise Unmarked--Ball-Jointed. Original clothes. 7-1/2"

MAKER: Made in Germany for George Borgfeldt, New York,
    N.Y., U.S.A.
DATE: 1929
MATERIAL: Ceramic head, cloth torso, composition arms and
    legs
MARK: "Gladdie Copyriht /sic7 Helen W. Jensen
                                Germany"
SIZES: 17" - 22"
DESIGNER: Helen W. Jensen

---

Marked Gladdie: Ceramic head, molded and painted hair, glass
    eyes, open-closed mouth w/molded teeth, laughing face,
    cloth torso, composition arms and legs; dressed; all in good
    condition.                      Size 17-22"   $450-600*
    Bisque Head, rare $600-800 *

*Not enough price samples
to justify a reliable range.

Illus. No. 78 "Gladdie Copyright
Helen W. Jensen
Germany"
18" Tall.

MAKER: Armand Marseille, J. D. Kestner, other German and
   French firms
DATE: Between World War I and World War II
MATERIAL: Bisque head, jointed composition body; some all
   bisque
MARK: Various
SIZE: Various

---

Googly-eyed Doll: Marked bisque head; original composition
   body jointed at neck, shoulders and hips; molded and
   painted socks and shoes, googly eyes look to side, sleep or
   set; impish mouth closed, proper wig, cute clothes; all in
   nice condition.
Marked A. M. (often mold 323). Size 7-8"  $250-325.
   Size   9"   $500-600.
Marked J. D. K. 221. $1,500 and up*
   *Not enough price samples to justify a reliable range.
All bisque painted eyes( unmarked, probably by Kestner)
Size 4-5" $200-250*

*Allow more for glass
eyes and/or swivel
neck.

> 1970
> Price Comparison
> Size 7-11" $122

Illus. No. 79 All Bisque
Googly

MAKER: Ludwig Greiner of Philadelphia, Penn., U.S.A.
DATE: 1858 to 1883
MATERIAL: Heads of papier-mâché; cloth bodies, homemade in
   most cases, but later some Lacmann bodies were used.
MARK: Paper label on back shoulder
   "Greiner's Improved Patent Heads, Pat. March 30th
   '58"
      "Greiner's Patent Doll Heads, No. 7, Pat. Mar. 30'58.
   Ext. '72"
SIZE: Various, 13" to over 35"

---

Greiner: Blond or black molded hair, painted features; complete
   late label, homemade cloth body, leather arms, nice old
   clothes; entire doll in nice condition. Size 16-24"$285-350*
   *Allow more for flirty and/or glass eyes.

| 1970 Price Comparison Size 21-32"$148 | Illus. No. 80 Left: "Greiners Patent Doll Heads Pat. Mar '58--Ext '72"  26"  Illus. No. 81 Right: 2nd mark above, 24" |

MAKER: Heinrich Handwerck of Waltershausen, Thüringia,
. Germany
DATE: Ca. 1890 - on
MATERIAL: Bisque head, composition ball-jointed body
MARK: "Germany - Handwerck" sometimes with "S & H" and
   numbers, such as 109, 119 etc.
SIZE: Various

---

Marked Handwerck Child Doll: Bisque socket head, ball-jointed
   body, open mouth, sleep or set eyes, original or good wig,
   pierced ears, lovely old clothes; entire doll in fine condition.

| | |
|---|---|
| Size 17-19" | $135-150 |
| Size 21-23" | $150-175 |
| Size 24-26" | $175-215 |
| Size 27-28" | $225-275 |
| Size 30-31" | $285-325 |
| Size 32-33" | $325-350 |
| Size 34-36" | $350-400 |

| 1970 Price Comparison | |
|---|---|
| Size 13-18" | $60 |
| Size 20-24" | $73 |
| Size 26-34" | $98 |

Illus. No. 82. Marked "11-1/2-99
DEP Germany
Handwerck Halbig"

"Heinrich Handwerck"
on body. 22 Inch.

# MAX HANDWERCK CHILD DOLL

MAKER: Max Handwerck of Waltershausen, Thüringia, Germany
DATE: 1900 - on
MATERIAL: Bisque socket head, ball-jointed composition body
MARK: "Max Handwerck" numbers and sometimes "Germany";
    also Bébé Elite
SIZE: Various

---

Marked Max Handwerck Child Doll: Marked bisque socket head;
    original or good wig, original ball-jointed body, pierced
    ears, set or sleep eyes, open mouth; well dressed; all in
    good shape.

Size 15-17" $125-135
Size 22-24" $150-185
Size 30"     $250

> 1970
> Price Comparison
> Size 14-28" $74

Illus. No. 83 Marked: "Max Handwerck Germany #203/2F5"
All Original--20 Inch.

MAKER: Edward Imeson Horsman Co. of New York, N.Y.
   (EIH), U.S.A.
DATE: 1925
MATERIAL: Composition; some all bisque
MARK: Sticker on foot
SIZE: Various
DESIGNER: Charles H. Twelvetrees

---

HEbee-SHEbee Doll: All-composition, jointed at shoulders and
  hips. Painted eyes; molded white chemise and real ties in
  molded blue shoes. Gummed label on foot. All in fine condition.  Size 10-1/2-12" $85-100

  All bisque, description as above. Size 4" $250 and up*
  *Not enough price samples to justify a reliable range.

1970 Price Comparison
Size 10-1/2-12"$35

Illus. No. 84 SHEbee
(unmarked) 4"Tall

# GEBRÜDER HEUBACH DOLLS

MAKER: Gebrüder Heubach of Licht and Sonneberg, Thüringia, Germany

DATE: Dolls considered here mostly from 1910 on

MATERIAL: Bisque head; kid or cloth or jointed composition body or composition bent-limb body

MARK: "Gebrüder Heubach - Germany"

SIZE: Various

---

Heubach Character Doll: Marked bisque head, character face, molded hair, intaglio eyes; jointed composition body; closed, open or open/closed mouth; dressed; all in nice condition.

Size 17-18"  $475-525
Size 13-15"  $350-400

Heubach Shoulder Head Doll: Marked bisque heads, character faces, good clothes; molded hair, intaglio eyes, closed or open/closed mouth; kid or cloth body, original or old bisque arms, cloth feet; all in good condition.  15-20"  $300-400

Heubach Infants: Marked bisque head, molded hair or good wig, character face, composition bent-limb body; open or closed mouth, sleep or intaglio eyes, dressed, all in nice condition. Size 8-12"  $200-300

---

1970 Price Comparison
Character
Size 5-14-1/2"  $91
Shoulder Head
Size 15-20"  $113
Infants
Size 7-20"  $68

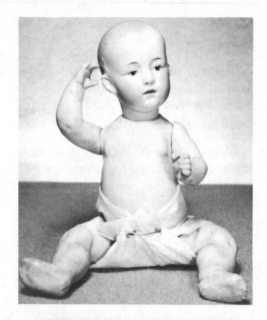

Illus. No. 85. Top left:
Gebrüder Heubach
Shoulder Head Doll Kid
Body--"Sunburst Mark
--2/0 Germany" 11-1/2"

Illus. No. 86. Top right:
Gebrüder Heubach
Infant "Sunburst Mark-
10-Germany" 7-1/4"
seated.

Illus. No. 87. Bottom
photo: | Heu |
" G-    | bach | Germany"
Ball-jointed Body 18".

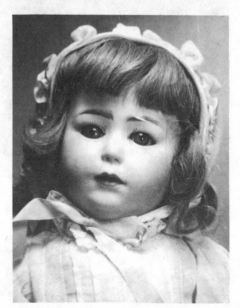

MAKER: Ernst Heubach of Köppelsdorf, Thüringia, Germany
DATE: Ca. late 1920's
MATERIAL: Black bisque head; black bent-limb composition or
    toddler body with composition arms and legs
MARK: "Heubach Köppelsdorf 399 - 16/0 Germany - D.R.G.M."
SIZE: Various

---

Heubach Köppelsdorf: Marked black bisque head, bent-limb or
    toddler black body, closed mouth, molded hair or black
    kinky wig, original grass skirt and brass jewelry, sleep
    eyes; all in fine condition.    Size 7-1/2 to 9-1/2" $225-325

> 1970 Price Comparison
> Size 7-1/2 to 10-1/2"
> $110

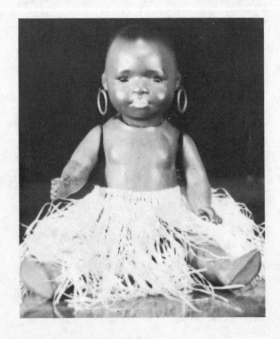

Illus. No. 88
"Heubach
Köppelsdorf
399 15/0 DRGM
Germany"
9-1/2"

MAKER: Ernst Heubach of Köppelsdorf, Thüringia, Germany
DATE: 1910 - on
MATERIAL: Bisque socket head, composition bent-limb baby or
   toddler body
MARK: "Heubach Köppelsdorf, Germany" and numbers, often
   300, 320, 342
SIZE: 8-25"

---

Marked Heubach Character Baby: Bisque socket head, good wig,
   sleep eyes, open mouth (wobbly tongue, pierced nostrils
   sometimes); composition bent-limb or toddler body; dressed;
   in good condition.  Size  9-12"  $135-150
                        Size 18-21"  $200-240
                        Size 22-24"  $225-295

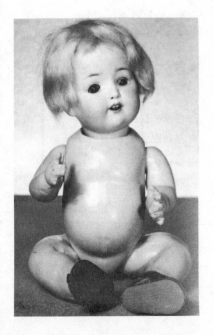

Illus. No. 89 Marked:
"Heubach Köppelsdorf--
   321-9/0 Germany"
   8 inch seated.

# HEUBACH KÖPPELSDORF CHILD DOLL

MAKER: Ernst Heubach of Köppelsdorf, Thüringia, Germany
DATE: 1887 - well into the 20th century
MATERIAL: Bisque head, jointed kid or jointed composition
 bodies
MARK: "Heubach Köppelsdorf, Germany" and sometimes
 horseshoe mark; numbers, often 275 (shoulder head) and 250
 (socket head)
SIZE: Various

---

Heubach Girl Doll: Marked bisque head, good wig, sleep eyes,
 open mouth, jointed composition body, cute clothes; all in
 nice condition.  Size 8-8-1/2"   $ 50- 60
                  Size 14-16"    $100-125
                  Size 20-24"    $140-175
Heubach Shoulder Head: Marked bisque head, kid or cloth body,
 bisque arms, sleep or set eyes, open mouth, good wig,
 dressed; all in nice condition. Size 11-13" $60- 75.
                  Size 14-20" $75-110.
                  Size 23-28"$125-175.

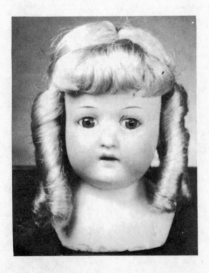

1970 Price Comparison
Girl Doll
Size 15-34"   $85
Shoulder Head
Size 14-24"   $41

Illus. No. 90.  Heubach
Shoulder head marked:
"Germany 275-11/0
Heubach Köppelsdorf"
Head 4 Inches Tall

MAKER: J.D. Kestner, Jr. of Waltershausen, Thüringia, Germany

DATE: 1914

MATERIAL: Bisque socket head, composition bent-limb baby body

MARK: "Made in Germany 245 JDK, Jr. 1914 © Hilda"; also sometimes 237 instead of 245

SIZE: Various

---

Kestner "Hilda": Marked bisque head, composition bent-limb baby body, good wig, sleep eyes, open mouth, dressed; all in good condition. Size 14-16"  $625-675
                                                    Size 20-23"  $850-950
Molded hair, large. $1,000-$1,200

Illus. No. 91 "JDK, Jr.
Hilda
245
©
1914
Germany"

MAKER: E.I. Horsman Inc., New York, N.Y., U.S.A.
DATE: Ca.1920's on
MATERIAL: Composition head, and curved arms and legs;
    stuffed cloth body, jointed at shoulders and hips
MARK: "H © C" embossed on back of neck and/or E.I.H. Co.
SIZE: Various

---

Marked Horsman Baby: Composition head with flange neck; body
    as described above; molded and painted hair, sleep eyes,
    open mouth, no teeth, original or good clothes; all in nice
    condition.                       Size 15-20"   $25-35.

Illus. No. 92 "Horsman Dolls" 18" Tall.

MAKER: Maison Huret, Paris, France
DATE: 1850 - 1920
MATERIAL: Heads - china or bisque; bodies - gutta percha,
   kid, wood or papier-mâché
MARK: "Huret", "Maison Huret" etc. on body
SIZE: Various

---

Marked Huret: China or bisque shoulder head, closed mouth,
   painted or glass eyes, good wig, kid or wooden jointed body,
   beautifully dressed; all in good condition. 18" $1250 and up*
   *Not enough price samples to justify a reliable range.

  *More for portrait face

> 1970 Price Comparison
> Size 14-18"  $725

Illus. No. 93 "Huret"
Portrait Face Jointed
Wood Body; Pewter
Hands. All Original
18"Tall

# INDIAN DOLL
### (North American Type)
### (Bisque Head)

MAKER: Armand Marseille of Köppelsdorf, Thüringia, Germany
and others.
DATE: Ca. 1894 - on
MATERIAL: Bisque head, jointed composition body
MARK: "A.M." - sometimes "Germany" - many unmarked
SIZE: Various

---

Indian Doll: Bisque head, composition body, jointed shoulders
and hips, entire doll light brown or "Indian copper color";
character face, worry wrinkles between brows, brown set
glass eyes, black wig in braids, original clothes, head
feathers, moccasins or molded shoes; all in nice condition.

| 1970 Price Comparison | Size 8-12" | $100-200 |
|---|---|---|
| Size 6-10"  $37 | Size   15" | $250 |

Illus. No. 94. Marked "Germany A.M. 5/0" 9-1/2"

### (Caucasian)

MAKER: Various Japanese firms
DATE: Ca. 1916 - on
MATERIAL: Bisque socket head, bent-limb composition body
MARK: "Nippon" or "Japan" sometimes "M.B." (Morimura
Bros.) or "F.Y."
SIZE: Various

---

Japanese Baby (Caucasian): Marked bisque head, bent-limb
composition body, mohair wig, sleep eyes, open mouth,
dressed; all in nice condition.

| | |
|---|---|
| Size 8-12" | $ 75-100 |
| Size 13-17" | $ 85-145 |
| Size 21-25" | $175-225 |

```
1970 Price Comparison
  Size 9-22"    $35
```

Illus. No. 91. Morimura
Bros. Baby Marked

"22 (M|B) Japan 2/0"

6-1/4"(seated)

# JAPANESE CHILD DOLL
### (Caucasian)

MAKER: Various Japanese firms
DATE: 1916 - on
MATERIAL: Bisque head, jointed kid or composition body
MARK: "Nippon" or "Japan", sometimes "M.B." (Morimura
    Bros.) or "F.Y."
SIZE: Various

---

Japanese Child Doll (Caucasian): Bisque head on ball-jointed
    composition or kid body, good wig, glass eyes, open mouth,
    nicely dressed; all in good condition. Size 15-20"   $65- 85
                                   Size 22-28"   $85-135

Illus. No. 96 Morimura
Bros. Japan Ball-
jointed body 23" tall.

MAKER: Alexander Doll Co., New York, N.Y., U.S.A.
DATE: 1942
MATERIAL: All composition
MARK: Body: "Alexander Pat. No. 2171281"
      Dress tag: "Jeannie Walker-Madame Alexander-
      N.Y. U.S.A. All rights reserved"
SIZE: 13" - 19"

---

Marked "Jeannie Walker": All composition with walking mechanism; sleep eyes, closed mouth, human hair or mohair wig,
dressed; all in good condition.     Size 13-19"    $55-75

Illus. No. 97
Jeannie
Walker
Original wig
Redressed
18" Tall.

94

# JULLIEN BÉBÉ

MAKER: Jullien, Jeune of Paris, France
DATE: 1875 to 1904 when they joined S.F.B.J.
MATERIAL: Bisque head, composition and wood body
MARK: "JULLIEN" with size number
SIZE: Various

---

Marked Jullien Bébé: Bisque head, jointed wood and composition
body; lovely wig, sleeping eyes, open mouth, pierced ears,
pretty old clothes; all in good condition.
Size 14" $300;   Size 21-25" $400;     Size 29"   $500-600
Same as above,but with closed mouth. 29"$1200-1400*
*Not enough price samples to justify a reliable range.

1970
Price
Comparison
Size 18-33"
$300

Illus. No. 98
"Jullien 12"
Ball-jointed Body
29"

# JUMEAU BÉBÉ

MAKER: Maison Jumeau, Paris. Later, Montreuil-sous-Bois, near Paris, France
DATE: Founded 1843 - Bébés Jumeau from ca. 1879 to 1899 - then through S.F.B.J.
MATERIAL: Bisque head, jointed papier-mâché body
MARK: "EJ", "TÊTE JUMEAU", "BÉBÉ JUMEAU" etc.
SIZE: Various

---

Bébé Jumeau: Marked bisque head, original marked papier-mâché body, original or good French wig, beautiful stationary eyes, closed mouth, pierced ears, original or lovely clothes; all in nice condition.

| | Size 12" | $525 |
|---|---|---|
| | Size 14-16" | $595-695 |
| | Size 18-21" | $750-850 |
| | Size 22-26" | $850-1050 |

Same as above but with open mouth; some are marked "1907"

| | Size 10-14" | $325-425 |
|---|---|---|
| | Size 18-24" | $350-460 |
| | Size 27-32" | $500-625 |

| 1970 Price Comparison | |
|---|---|
| Size 13-19" | $328 |
| Size 20-25" | $353 |
| Size 27-35" | $464 |
| Open Mouth | |
| Size 14-24" | $217 |
| Size 30-36" | $300 |

Illus. No. 99. On Head--
"Breveté S.G.D.G. Jumeau 10"
On Body--"Jumeau Medaille D'or, Paris"

# JUMEAU BÉBÉ
### (Long-face or Cody)

MAKER: Maison Jumeau, Paris. Later, Montreuil-sous-Bois, near Paris, France
DATE: Ca. 1887
MATERIAL: Bisque head, jointed papier-mâché body
MARK: Number only on head; "Jumeau Medaille D'or", on body
SIZE: Various

---

Long-face Jumeau: Number only on bisque head, marked body, beautiful wig, closed mouth, applied pierced ears, blown glass eyes, straight wrists, lovely clothes; all in good condition.   Size 24-28"   $2,000-$3,000*
*Not enough price samples to justify a reliable range.

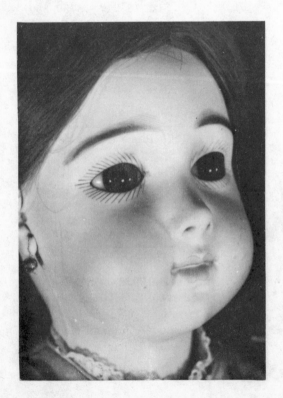

1970
Price
Comparison
Size 16-32"
$385

Illus. No. 100
Long-face Jumeau
24" Tall.

**(Metal Head)**

MAKER: Karl Standfuss, Deuben near Dresden, Saxony, Germany
DATE: 1904 - on
MATERIAL: Metal shoulder head, bodies used of various
    materials
MARK: JUNO     on chest
SIZE: Various

---

Marked JUNO: Metal shoulder head, molded features and hair,
    painted or set glass eyes, kid, cloth or kidette jointed body,
    bisque or composition hands, dressed; all in good condition.

Size 17-22"    $65-85

1970 Price Comparison
Size 18-20"   $48

Illus. No. 101 Marked
Juno--18 inch

# JUST ME DOLL

MAKER: Armand Marseille of Köppelsdorf, Thüringia, Germany
DATE: Ca. 1925
MATERIAL: Bisque socket head, composition jointed body
MARK: "Just Me A. M. 310 Germany"
SIZE: Various

---

Marked "Just Me": Bisque socket head, eyes to side, closed
   mouth, curly wig, composition body, dressed; all in good
   condition.    Size 10" $300-400*
   *Not enough price samples to justify a reliable range.
   Same as above with <u>painted</u> bisque head; all original.
   Size 8" $125-135.

Illus. No. 102. "Just
Me A. M. 310
Germany"
Painted Bisque Head
All Original. 8" Tall.

MAKER: Cuno and Otto Dressel, Sonneberg, Thüringia,
    Germany. Heads by Simon & Halbig and others
DATE: 1906 - 1921
MATERIAL:Bisque head, composition ball-jointed body.
MARK: "Jutta S & H" also numbers 1348 and 1349
SIZE: Various

---

Marked S & H Jutta: Bisque socket head, open mouth, sleep
    eyes, pierced ears, good wig, ball-jointed composition body;
    dressed; all in good condition.         Size 17-20"   $175-195
                                            Size 24-26"   $200-250

Illus. No. 103. "Jutta 1329 S&H" 17" Tall.

MAKER: K & K Toy Co., New York, N.Y. Owned and controlled
　　by George Borgfeldt.
DATE: 1918
MATERIAL: Bisque heads, made in Thüringia; cloth body,
　　composition arms made in U.S.
MARK: "Germany K & K 60 Thüringia" also mold numbers 45
　　and 56
SIZE: Various

---

Marked K & K Child Doll: Bisque shoulder head, cloth body,
　　composition arms, beautiful wig, open mouth, sleep eyes,
　　dressed; all in good condition.　　Size 17-24"　$120-185

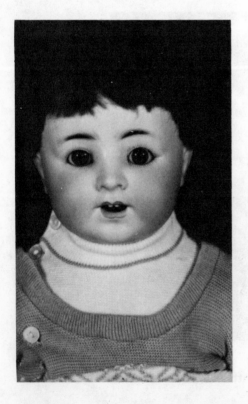

```
1970
Price Comparison
Size 20-24"　$55
```

Illus. No.104
"Germany
K&K
60
Thüringia"
22" Tall

MAKER: Kämmer & Reinhardt of Waltershausen, Thüringia,
    Germany
DATE: 1909 - on
MATERIAL: Bisque head, composition bent-limb body
MARK: "K (star) R #100"
SIZE: Various

---

Marked Kaiser Baby: Solid dome bisque head, original composition bent-limb body, intaglio eyes, dressed, open/closed
mouth, all in good shape.

| | | |
|---|---|---|
| Size 11-14" | $300-350 |
| Size 15" | $350-395 |
| Size 18-19" | $475-575 |

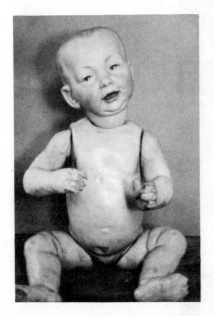

1970 Price Comparison
Various Sizes $168

Illus. No. 105 Kaiser Baby
K(star)R # 100

MAKER: Louise R. Kampes Studios, Atlantic City, N.J., U.S.A.
DATE: Ca. 1920
MATERIAL: Molded mask face, cloth stuffed torso and limbs
MARK: "Kamkins, a dolly made to love.
      Patented by L.R. Kampes.
      Atlantic City, N.J." on head
SIZE: Various

---

Marked "Kamkins": Molded mask face with painted features,
    wig, cloth body and limbs, dressed, all in good condition.

   Size 18-19" $150-200*
   *Not enough price samples to justify a reliable range.

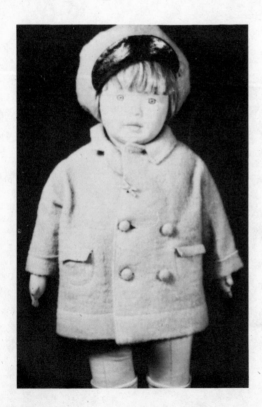

Illus. No. 106
"Kamkins" Signed
on head as above.
All original 19" tall.

MAKER: Kämmer & Reinhardt of Waltershausen, Thüringia, Germany
DATE: 1909 - on
MATERIAL: Bisque head, composition bent-limb body
MARK: "K(star)R", sometimes with numbers, such as 126, 121, 122, 128 "S & H", and many times "Germany"
SIZE: Various

---

Marked K(star)R Baby: Bisque head, original or good wig, sleep eyes, open mouth, composition bent-limb body, nicely dressed, may have voice box or spring tongue; all in good condition.

| | | |
|---|---|---|
| Mold #126: | Size 11-15" | $150-195 |
| | Size 16-21" | $200-285 |
| | Size 23-24" | $300-375 |
| Mold#121: | Size 12" | $225 |
| | Size 22" | $350 |
| Mold #122: | Size 18-20" | $350 |
| Mold#128: | Size 18-20" | $350 |

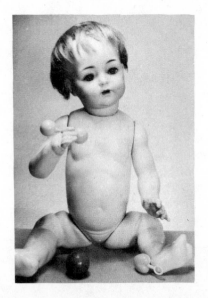

| 1970 Price Comparison |  |
|---|---|
| Size 10-14" | $50 |
| Size 18-24" | $65 |

Illus. No. 107 K(star)R
Simon Halbig
121
36
12-1/2"seated

MAKER: Kämmer & Reinhardt of Waltershausen, Thüringia,
   Germany
DATE: 1910 on
MATERIAL: Bisque socket head, composition ball-jointed body
MARK: "K (star) R", sometimes with "S & H", often "Germany".
   Numbers, such as 101, 107, 109, 114, 117, 116A
SIZE: Various                                    K. ✡ R.

---

Marked K(star)R Character Doll: Bisque socket head, good wig,
   painted or glass eyes, closed mouth, composition ball-
   jointed body, nicely dressed; all in good condition.
   Mold #117: Size      22"            $950*
   Mold #101: Size      15"        $900-1,000*
   Mold #114: Size 12-14"      $1,000-1,200*
   Mold #116A Size 20-24"       $900-1,000*
   *Not enough price samples to justify a reliable range.

Illus. No. 108 K(star)R
117
S&H
Germany"
22" Tall.

# K (STAR) R CHILD DOLL

MAKER: Kämmer & Reinhardt of Waltershausen, Thüringia, Germany
DATE: 1895 began use of "K (star) R" mark
MATERIAL: Bisque head, composition ball-jointed body
MARK: "K (star) R", sometimes with "S & H", and many times "Germany", often "403"
SIZE: Various
DESIGNER: Karl Krauser, after 1901

---

Marked K(star)R Child Doll: Bisque head, original or good wig, sleep eyes, open mouth, pierced ears, dressed, ball-jointed composition body; all in good condition.

| | |
|---|---|
| Size 19-22" | $145-160 |
| Size 24-25" | $165-200 |
| Size 28-29" | $225-295 |
| Size 32-34" | $350-395 |

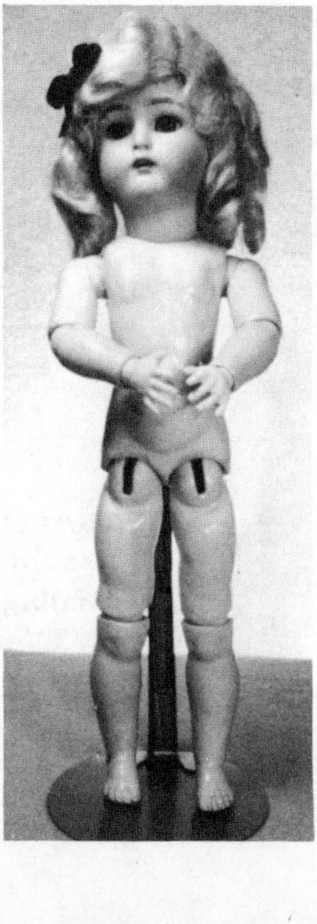

| 1970 Price Comparison | |
|---|---|
| Size 7-1/2-10" | $37 |
| Size 20-25" | $92 |

Illus. No. 109 Marked "K(star)R Halbig--39" 14-1/2 inches.

MAKER: Kämmer & Reinhardt, Waltershausen, Thüringia, Germany
DATE: 1908 - "The Flirt" advertised
MATERIAL: Bisque head, composition bent-limb baby or ball-jointed toddler body
MARK: "K(star)R" and many times "Germany", often 126
SIZE: Various
DESIGNER: Karl Krauser

---

Marked Flirty-Eye: Bisque head, sleep and flirting eyes, open mouth, good wig, composition body, nicely dressed; all in good condition.          Mold#126: Size 13-15"  $195-225
                                         Size 16-17"  $225-275
                                         Size 22-23"  $375-395

| 1970 Price Comparison Size 18-23" $95 |
|---|

Illus. No. 110
"K(Star)R Simon
& Halbig 126"
12-1/2" seated.

MAKER: Kämmer & Reinhardt, Waltershausen, Thüringia, Germany

DATE: Toddlers (with chubby jointed composition bodies) probably originated in the second decade of the 20th century

MATERIAL: Bisque head, composition toddler bodies, some ball-jointed, some with fewer joints

MARK: "K(star)R", sometimes with "S & H", #121, 122, or 126, 128; some with "Germany"

SIZE: Various·

---

Marked K(star)R Toddler: Bisque head, composition toddler body, sleep eyes, original mohair wig or good replacement, open mouth, sweetly dressed; all in nice condition.

Size 14-16"    $225-275
Size 20-25"    $350-395

| 1970 |
|---|
| Price Comparison |
| Size 10-18"    $85 |
| Size 20-28"    $122 |

Illus. No. 111
K(star)R
Simon Halbig
126-23
Toddler Body
9-1/2 inch.

MAKER: J. D. Kestner, Jr. of Waltershausen, Thüringia,
Germany
DATE: 1910 - on
MATERIAL: Bisque head, composition bent-limb body
MARK: "J.D.K.", sometimes numbers such as 211, 152, 257,
142 and "Germany"
SIZE: Various

---

Marked Kestner Baby: Bisque head, molded and/or painted hair;
bent-limb body, open or open/closed mouth, sleep eyes or
set, well dressed; nice condition.

| | | |
|---|---|---|
| Solid Dome Head: | Size 9-12" | $155-250 |
| | Size 16-18" | $250-315 |
| | Size 21-25" | $350-395 |
| Mold #211(wig): | Size 10-13" | $225-235 |
| | Size 15-17" | $225-275 |
| | Size 23" | $350 |
| Mold #257(wig) | | |
| | Size 13-15" | $195-235 |
| | Size 23-25" | $325-425 |
| Mold #152(wig) | | |
| | Size 15-18" | $175-250 |

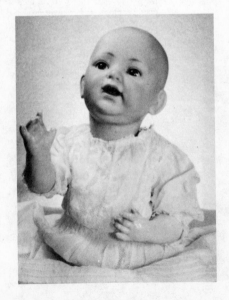

1970 Price Comparison
Size 11-1/2-15" $80
Size 16-26" $115

Illus. No. 112 Marked
"J.D.K. 5 Made
in Germany"
11 inch(seated)

MAKER: J.D. Kestner, Jr. of Waltershausen, Thüringia, Germany

DATE: Ca. 1880

MATERIAL: Bisque socket head, ball-jointed composition body or bisque shoulder head on kid body w/bisque arms

MARK: Sometimes numbers

SIZE: Various

---

Kestner Closed-mouth Child: Bisque head, closed mouth, paperweight eyes, good wig, body as above, well dressed; all in good condition.

| | |
|---|---|
| Size 18" | $400 |
| Size 24-28" | $500 |
| Character Face--18-21" $650 | |

Illus. No. 113.
Unmarked probable
Kestner
Jointed Composition
Body.

# KESTNER CHILD DOLL
## (J.D.K.)

MAKER: J.D. Kestner, Jr. of Waltershausen, Thüringia, Germany
DATE: Late 1880's to ca. 1940
MATERIAL: Bisque head, composition ball-jointed body
MARK: Numbers such as 171, 146, 164, 195 etc., along with A 5, B6, C7, etc. and often "Made in Germany"
SIZE: Various

---

Kestner Child Doll: Marked bisque head, original ball-jointed body, original or good wig, sleep eyes, open mouth, well dressed; all in nice condition.

| | |
|---|---|
| Size 17-19" | $140-150 |
| Size 22-24" | $165-195 |
| Size 29-32" | $285-325 |

| 1970 Price Comparison | |
|---|---|
| Size 16-24" | $66 |
| Size 25-28" | $85 |
| Size 30-38" | $142 |

Illus. No.114
"M Made
in Germany
16"
146
29 inches.

## (J.D.K.)

MAKER: J. D. Kestner of Waltershausen, Thüringia, Germany
DATE: 1880 to ca. 1920
MATERIAL: Bisque shoulder head, jointed kid body, bisque arms, kid or cloth feet.
MARK: Numbers such as 154, 159, etc.; sometimes "Made in Germany"
SIZE: Various

---

Kestner Kid Body Doll: Marked bisque shoulder head, jointed kid body, bisque arms, kid or cloth legs, original or good wig, sleep or set eyes, open mouth, nicely dressed, all in good condition.

Size 17-19"    $105-135
Size 20-26"    $125-200

| 1970 Price Comparison | |
|---|---|
| Size 14-18" | $59 |
| Size 21-34" | $132 |

Illus. No. 115 "4-1/2 0
159 DEP 8-1/2 0 "
On head "JDK" Crown
& Streamers on
front of Kid Body.

MAKER: J. D. Kestner, Jr. of Waltershausen, Thüringia, Germany
DATE: Ca. 1910
MATERIAL: Bisque shoulder head, kid body or bisque socket head, composition ball-jointed lady body
MARK: Socket head: "162 Made in Germany"
 Shoulder head: "Made in Germany" (sometimes "Gibson Girl" on kid body)
SIZE: Various

---

Kestner "Gibson Girl":Bisque shoulder head with <u>closed</u> mouth, uplifted chin, glass eyes, good wig. Kid body with bisque lower arms. Beautifully dressed. All in good condition. Size 21" $1200-1800*
*Not enough price samples to justify a reliable range.

For picture of "Gibson Girl" see:<u>Collector's Encyclopedia of Dolls</u> by Dorothy, Elizabeth and Evelyn Coleman. Page 351
Kestner 162: Bisque socket head, open mouth, sleep eyes, good wig. Mature-type face. Adult body completely ball-jointed. Beautifully dressed. All in good condition. Size 18" $300-400*
*Not enough price samples for reliable range.

For picture of Kestner 162 see:<u>Collector's Encyclopedia of Dolls</u> by Dorothy, Elizabeth and Evelyn Coleman. Page 350

MAKERS: J. D. Kestner and other Germany companies (bisque and celluloid), United States (composition), Japan (copies in all three materials)

DATE: 1913 - on

MATERIALS: Those mentioned above as well as bisque heads for cloth bodies and bisque heads found on chubby toddler ball-jointed composition bodies.

MARK: "O'NEILL" - incised on sole of foot; and/or red and gold heart shape "KEWPIE O'NEILL" label on chest, and/or round label on back - "Copyright ROSE O'NEILL"

SIZE: Various

DESIGNER: Rose O'Neill, U.S.A.

U.S. AGENT: George Borgfeldt & Co., New York, N.Y., U.S.A.

---

Marked Bisque Kewpie: Standing, legs together, arms jointed, blue wings, painted features, eyes to side, good condition.

Size 4-6" $50-75*

*Allow extra for action poses.

| 1970 Price Comparison |
|---|
| Size 4-1/2-7-1/2"   $43 |
| Size 8-9"     $87 |

Illus. No. 116
Marked Bisque
Kewpie 4-1/2 inch.

# KEWPIE—CELLULOID
℗    (O'Neill)

MAKER: Karl Standfuss, Deuben near Dresden, Saxony, Germany
DATE: Ca. 1913 - on
MATERIAL: All celluloid - flesh color; all celluloid - black
(Hottentots)
MARK: Gummed labels, front or back, etc.
SIZE: Various
DESIGNER: Rose O'Neill, U.S.A.
U.S. AGENT: George Borgfeldt & Co. of New York, N.Y.

---

Marked Celluloid Kewpies: Flesh colored Kewpie, straight
standing, arms jointed, has blue wings, legs together; OR
black Kewpie Hottentot with white painted wings, jointed
arms, legs together; all in mint condition.

|  |  |
|---|---|
| Size 4- 7" | $15-25 |
| Size 8-10" | $55-75 |

| 1970 Price Comparison |  |
|---|---|
| Size 4-1/2-7" | $15 |
| Size 8-10" | $23 |

For Picture of "Hottentots" see: Collector's Encyclopedia of
Dolls, Dorothy, Elizabeth, Evelyn Coleman. Page 306

MAKERS: Rex Doll Co., New York, N.Y., Mutual Doll Co., New York, N.Y., also Cameo Doll Co., New York, N.Y. (1922) U.S.A.

DATE: Ca. 1913

MATERIAL: Composition

MARKS: Heart-shaped labels on chest etc.

SIZE: Various

DESIGNER: Rose O'Neill , U.S.A

U.S. AGENT: George Borgfeldt & Co., New York, N.Y., and others

---

O'Neill Kewpie: Marked composition Kewpie, swivel or stationary head, movable arms, stationary or movable legs, blue wings, painted features, eyes to side; all in good condition.                     Size 11-13"        $45-55

1970
Price
Comparison
Size 11-13"   $25

Illus. No. 117
Composition Kewpie
with
Blue Wings and
Label
11-1/2 inch.

MAKER: Kley & Hahn of Ohrdruf, Thüringia, Germany
DATE: Ca. 1910
MATERIAL: Bisque head, composition bent-limb body
MARK: K & H "Germany"; numbers, such as 158, 167, 266
SIZE: Various

---

Marked Kley & Hahn Baby: Bisque head, bald or wigged, bent-limb body, sleep or intaglio eyes, open/closed mouth. Fully dressed, all in nice condition.

| | |
|---|---|
| Size 12-13" | $175-195 |
| Size 16-19" | $200-275 |
| Size 22" | $325 |

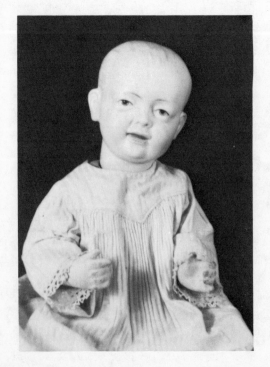

1970
Price
Comparison
Size 12-19" $88

Illus. No. 118
"Germany
K&H
625"
Open-closed mouth,
painted eyes
14-1/2" tall.

MAKER: Gebrüder Knoch of Neustadt near Coburg, Thüringia,
  Germany
DATE: Ca. 1908
MATERIAL: Bisque heads, composition stick-type jointed
  bodies

MARK:  "Made in Germany";  numbers, such as
        D E P        201,199,192
SIZE: Various

---

Marked Knoch Child Doll: Bisque head, mohair wig, open mouth,
  sleep eyes, dressed, composition and wood stick-type body.
  Good condition.        Size 12-14"    $75-95

1970 Price Comparison
Size 11-1/2-14"$39

Illus. No. 119

201

Made in Germany
DE P"
12" tall.

**KRAUSS CHILD DOLL**
**(G br K)**

MAKER: Gebrüder Krauss of Eisfeld, Thüringia, Germany
DATE: Ca. 1907
MATERIAL: Bisque head, ball-jointed composition body

MARK:   Numbers such as 165 and "Germany"

SIZE: Various

---

Marked Krauss Child Doll: Bisque head, ball-jointed body, sleep
eyes, open mouth, good mohair wig, dressed, all in good
condition.  Size 21-26"  $135-175

> 1970 Price Comparison
> Size 22-29"  $83

Illus. No.120 Head of Krauss child doll. Marked on back of head.

MAKER: Käthe Kruse, Berlin, Germany
DATE: 1910 - on
MATERIAL: Molded muslin head (hand painted), jointed cloth
   body
MARK:"Käthe Kruse on sole of foot, sometimes also "Germany"
   and a number
SIZE: Various

---

Marked Käthe Kruse: Jointed at shoulders and hips, suitably
   dressed, in good condition.     Size 17-20"   $125-175

> 1970 Price Comparison
> Size 14-17"  $65

Illus. No. 121 Left doll:"Käthe Kruse 20204 Germany" 17"tall.
Right doll: Lenci 13" tall.

# LENCI
## (Scavini)

MAKER: Enrico & Signora Scavini, Italy
DATE: 1920 - on
MATERIAL: Pressed felt head with painted features, jointed
    felt bodies (later cloth)
MARK: "LENCI" on tags
SIZE: 5" to 45"

---

Felt Lenci: All original clothing, tags, marked etc., all in good
    condition.        Lady doll, bed-type. Size 24-29"  $100-150
                      Child doll. Size 10-12"  $ 65- 90
                                  Size 16-18"  $100-125
                      Character Portrait. Size 20-24"  $200-295

| 1970 Price Comparison | |
|---|---|
| Size 9-12" | $28 |
| Size 16-23" | $44 |

Illus. No. 122
Lenci, 13" All original.

MAKER: A Lanternier & Cie. of Limoges, France
DATE: Ca. 1891 to ca. 1914
MATERIAL: Bisque head, papier-mâché body
MARK: Anchor with "Limoges A. L. -- France" or
    "Fabrication Française A. L. & Co. Limoges", sometimes
    "Cherie", etc.
SIZE: Various

---

Marked Limoges Child: Bisque head, papier-mâché jointed body,
    good or original wig, large stationary eyes, open mouth,
    pierced ears, pretty clothes; all in good condition.
    Size 19-24"    $225-325

> 1970
> Price
> Comparison
> Size 17-33"
> $112

Illus. No. 123
Marked
"Fabrication
Française
A. L. & Co.
Limoges"
13-1/2"

# LOVUMS
## (EFFanBEE)

MAKER: Bernard E. Fleischaker and Hugo Baum of New York,
N.Y., U.S.A.
DATE: Ca. 1928 to 1939
MATERIAL: Composition head, arms and legs; cloth body.
MARK: "LOVUMS" &"EFFanBEE"
SIZE: Various

---

Marked LOVUMS: Composition shoulder head, arms and legs;
pretty face, smiling open mouth with teeth, molded painted
hair or wig, sleep eyes, cloth body, nicely dressed; all in
good condition.                Size 20"          $45-50

1970
Price
Comparison
Size18-22"
$18

Illus. No. 124
"Lovums
Effanbee "
25"tall.

MAKER: Armand Marseille of Köppelsdorf, Thüringia, Germany
DATE: 1910 - on
MATERIAL: Bisque head, bent-limb composition body
MARK: "A.M." and/or "ARMAND MARSEILLE" plus
    "Germany" and numbers such as 990, 992, 985, etc.
SIZE: Various

---

Marked A.M. Baby: Bisque head, composition bent-limb body,
    sleep eyes, open mouth - some with teeth, good wig,
    suitably dressed; all in nice condition.
    Mold #990, #971 and other common numbers.

| | |
|---|---|
| Size 5-1/2-9-1/2" | $ 75-125 |
| Size 11-13" | $125-150 |
| Size 15-16" | $150-175 |
| Size 18-19" | $165-210 * |

*Allow extra for less
common mold
numbers 326, 500 etc.

Mold #992:
    Size 13-18"
    $175-225

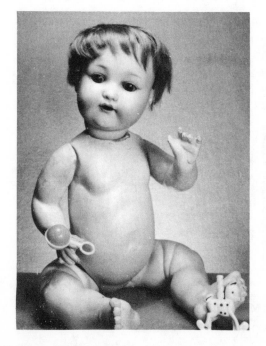

1970
Price
Comparison
Size 11-14"$41
Baby Wig
Size 8-19" $46

Illus. No. 125
Marked "Otto Gans
Germany 975 A. 6M".
12 inch(seated)

# A.M. CHILD DOLL
### (Ball-jointed)

MAKER: Armand Marseille of Köppelsdorf, Thüringia, Germany
DATE: Ca. 1890 - on
MATERIAL: Bisque head, composition ball-jointed body
MARK: "A. M." and/or "ARMAND MARSEILLE" plus numbers,
   such as 390, 1894, etc., and/or "Germany"
SIZE: Various

---

Marked A.M. Child Doll: Bisque head, composition ball-jointed
   body, nice wig, set or sleep eyes, open mouth, pretty
   clothes; all in good condition.   Mold #390 Size 7-9"     $50-65

| 1970 Price Comparison Mold #390 | |
|---|---|
| Size  7-12" | $37 |
| Size 21-33" | $76 |

Size 10-12"     $60- 85
Size 16-19"     $85-125
Size 20-25"   $125-165
Size 28-30"   $185-225
Size 33-36"   $300-350
Mold#1894 slightly higher

Illus.no.126 Left:"Armand Marseille Germany 390 A.7-1/2 M."25"
Illus.no.127 Right: "1894 A.M.2/0 DEP" 11 inch.

MAKER: Armand Marseille of Köppelsdorf, Thüringia, Germany
DATE: 1924 on
MATERIAL: Bisque head, cloth or sometimes composition body
MARK: A.M. 351 (open mouth) or 341 (closed mouth)
SIZE: Various

---

Marked A.M. Infant: Solid dome bisque head with molded and/or
    painted hair, sleep eyes, open mouth with teeth, cloth or
    composition body, all in good condition. Dressed.
Mold #341(Closed Mouth, so-called Dream Baby)
    Size  9-12"    $125-150
    Size 14-16"    $150-225
Mold #351(Open Mouth, so-called Rockabye Baby)
    Size  7-12"    $135-157
    Size 15-16"    $160-175
    Size 19-23"    $265-350

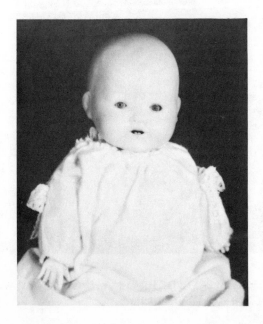

Illus. No. 128
"A.M.  351"
Rockabye  Baby
16"tall

**A.M. KID BODY DOLL**

MAKER: Armand Marseille, Köppelsdorf, Thüringia, Germany
DATE: Ca. 1890 - on
MATERIAL: Bisque shoulder head, jointed kid body with bisque
  lower arms.
MARK: "A. M." and/or "Armand Marseille" plus numbers,
  such as 370, 3200, 3500, etc., and/or "Germany"; also
  sometimes horseshoe mark.
SIZE: Various

---

A. M. Kid Body Doll: Marked bisque shoulder head; jointed kid
  body, bisque lower arms, sleep or set eyes, open mouth,
  pretty costume; all in nice condition. Size 11-12"     $75- 95
                                                         Size 16-20"   $100-135
  ┌─────────────────────────────┐                       Size 23-26"   $150-185
  │  1970 Price Comparison       │
  │  Size 11-16" $39    18-28"$65 │
  └─────────────────────────────┘

Illus. no. 129 Left:"No.3500 AM 2-1/2 DE P.Made in Germany"
Illus. no. 130 Right:"AM 370 3/0 DEP" 14 inch.

MAKER: D. M. Smith & Co., Springfield, Vt., U.S.A.

DATE: 1881 to 1893

MATERIAL: Composition heads, wood body, arms and legs. Hands and feet made of pewter or lead. Older type had spoon hands and wooden feet.

MARK: None unless black paper band carrying patent dates is still around waist

SIZE: 12 inches

---

Marked Mason and Taylor Doll: Composition head, wood body, legs and arms; hands and feet usually of metal, fully jointed, dressed; in fair condition. (depending on condition) $250 and up*

*Not enough price samples to justify a reliable range.

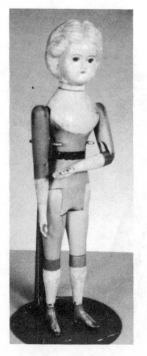

| 1970 |
| Price Comparison |
| Size 12" $125 |

Illus. No. 131
Mason and Taylor
12 inch.

# MILLINER'S MODEL
### (So-called)

MAKER: Unknown German firms
DATE: Ca. 1820's into the 1850's
MATERIAL: Papier-mâché shoulder heads, stiff slender kid
    bodies, wooden extremities
MARK: None
SIZE: Various

---

Milliner's Model: Unretouched shoulder head, various molded
    hairdos, original kid body, wooden arms and legs, painted
    features, eyes blue, black or brown. Original or very old
    handmade clothing; entire doll in good condition.
    Size 6-12" $165-285*
    *Some types much more expensive than others depending
    upon rarity of hair style and condition.

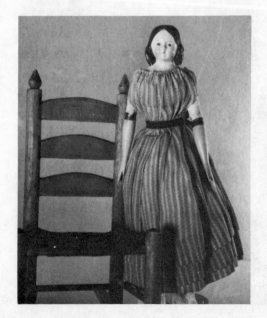

1970
Price
Comparison
Size 9-1/2-12"
$127
Size 14-20" $189

Illus. No. 132
Milliner's Model
Ca 1830 12-1/2"

MAKER: Buschow & Beck of Nossen, Saxony, Germany
DATE: Ca. 1894 - on
MATERIAL: Metal shoulder head, kid or cloth body
MARK: "Minerva -- Germany" also embossed helmet
SIZE: Various
AGENTS: A. Vischer & Co. of New York, N.Y. and Louis
    Wolf & Co. of Boston, Mass. and New York, N.Y., U.S.A.

---

Marked Minerva Head: Metal shoulder head, kid or cloth body,
    bisque or composition hands, painted eyes, molded blond
    wavy hair, dressed; nice unretouched condition.
    Size 12-15"   $45-55*
    *Allow extra for glass eyes.

> 1970
> Price
> Comparison
> Size 8-1/2-15"
> $22.50

Illus. No. 133
Marked "Minerva
(with helmet)
Germany" 13 inch.

# MON TRÉSOR DOLL

MAKER: Henri Rostal, Paris, France
DATE: 1914
MATERIAL: Bisque head, ball-jointed composition body
MARK: "Mon Trésor"
SIZE: Various

---

Marked "Mon Trésor": Bisque socket head, sleep eyes, open
mouth with teeth, good wig, pierced ears, ball-jointed composition body; dressed; all in good condition.

Size 17-21"    $275-300

# NEW BORN BABE
### (Amberg)

MAKER: Louis Amberg & Son, New York, N.Y., U.S.A.
DATE: 1914; Reissued 1924
MATERIAL: Bisque head, cloth body
MARK: "© L.A. & S. 1914, G 45520 Germany #4" also "]
    copyrighted by LOUIS AMBERG and SON"
SIZE: Various
DESIGNER: Jeno Juszko

---

New Born Babe: Marked bisque head, cloth body, celluloid,
    rubber or composition hands; painted bald head, sleep eyes,
    closed mouth, nicely dressed; all in good condition.

| | |
|---|---|
| Size 8-9" | $135-150 |
| Size 11-1/2" | $175-195 |
| Size 14-16" | $295 |

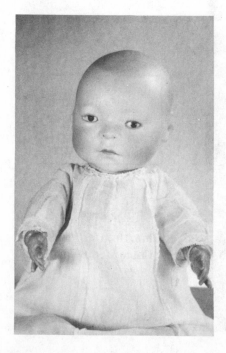

| 1970 Price Comparison |
|---|
| Size 8-1/2-16"   $ 65 |

Illus. No. 134 Marked
New Born Babe
11inch (seated)

MAKER: Various German firms
DATE: Ca. 1860's thru 1870's
MATERIAL: Fine parian bisque shoulder head, cloth or kid
    body; leather, wood, china or combination extremities
MARK: None
SIZE: Various

---

Unmarked Parian: Pale or untinted shoulder head; pierced ears,
    closed mouth, beautifully molded hairdo, painted eyes,
    cloth body, lovely clothes; entire doll in fine condition.
    Size 10-15"    $125-185
    Size 16-23"    $185-275*
    *Allow extra for unusual molded details, such as hair style,
    flowers, or necklace, etc.
    *Glass eyes are rare.

1970
Price Comparison
Size 9- 13-1/2"
$130
Size 15-24"$166

Illus. No. 135 Parian
Unmarked 8-3/4"

MAKER: Parsons - Jackson Co. of Cleveland, Ohio, U.S.A.
DATE: 1910 to 1919
MATERIAL: Biskoline (similar to celluloid) jointed with steel
    springs
MARKS: Embossed figure of small stork on back of head and
    also on back of shoulders with "PARSONS-JACKSON,
    CLEVELAND, OHIO" under that.
SIZE: Various

---

Marked Parsons-Jackson Baby or Toddler: Socket head and
    bent-limb baby or toddler type of Biskoline; molded-painted
    hair, painted eyes, spring joint construction. Nicely
    dressed; all in nice condition.      Size 12"      $75-85

| 1970 Price Comparison |
|---|
| Size 10-14"  $55 |

Illus. No. 136: Left: Parsons-Jackson
  Biskoline Baby 7"(seated)
Illus. No. 137: Right: Same doll--back
  view showing raised mark .

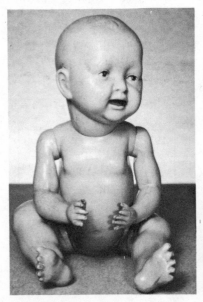
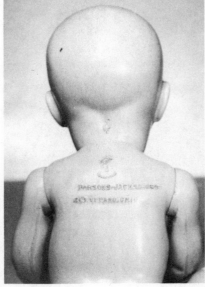

# PATSY DOLLS
## (EFFanBEE)

MAKER: EFFanBEE Doll Corp., New York, N.Y., U.S.A.
   (Bernard Fleischaker & Hugo Baum)
DATE: 1926 - on
MATERIAL: Composition, jointed at neck, shoulders and hips
MARK: "EFFanBEE PATSY DOLL" across back of shoulders
   "Patsy Lou", "Patsy-Ann", "Patsy Joan","Wee Patsy" etc.
SIZE: 5-3/4" to 22"
DESIGNER: Bernard Lipfert

---

Marked Patsy: All composition, sleep eyes, closed mouth,
   molded hair. Nicely dressed; good condition.

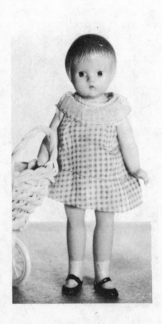

| | |
|---|---|
| 5-1/2" Wee Patsy | $65-75 |
| 8" Patsy Baby-ette | $40-45 |
| 9" Patsyette | $35-40 |
| 11" Patsy, Jr. | $40-45 |
| 13" Patsy | $30-45 |
| 13" Patsy Baby | $40-45 |
| 14" Patricia | $45-55 |
| 16" Patsy Joan | $55-60 |
| 18" Patsy Ann | $50-60 |
| 22" Patsy Lou | $65-75 |
| 26" Patsy Ruth | $125 |

NOTE:Allow extra for
original clothes, wig, or
Effanbee bracelet.

| 1970 Price Comparison |
|---|
| Marked Patsy |
| Size 5-3/4-13"  $25 |
| Size 14-22"  $30 |

Illus. No.138 Marked Wee
   Patsy 5-3/4 inch.

MAKER: Various German and English Craftsmen
DATE: Late 18th to early 20th century
MATERIAL: All wood, ball-jointed or pegged
MARK: None
SIZE: One-half inch up

---

Late 18th and Early 19th Century: Finely carved wooden head, glass eyes, wig or carved and painted hair, jointed wooden body. *These are seldom available and could cost $1,000 or more.

Mid - Late 19th Century: Carved wooden head, painted hair and eyes, jointed wooden body, dressed; in good condition.

Size 9" $50-85

Early 20th Century: Wooden head, painted hair, eyes and features, carved nose, peg-jointed at shoulders, elbows, hips and knees, dressed; in good condition. Size 12" $5-25.

Illus. No. 139
Early 20th Century Penny Wooden 12" (including stand)

# PETITE FRANÇAISE
### (J. Verlingue)

MAKER: J. Verlingue of Boulogne-sur-Mer, France
DATE: 1914 to ca. 1919
MATERIAL: Bisque head, papier-mâché body

MARK: "PETITE FRANÇAISE -- FRANCE"

SIZE: Various

---

Marked Petite Française: Bisque head, jointed papier-mâché
body; good wig, glass eyes, open mouth, nicely dressed.
Size 18-20"  $275-300

1970
Price
Comparison
Size 8-12"  $50
Size 16-20"  $75

Illus. No. 140
Marked "Petite
Française
(anchor)J. V. France
6"
17-1/2 inch

MAKER: Unknown U.S. firm
DATE: First half of 1800's
MATERIAL: Papier-mâché shoulder head; stuffed cloth body,
    mostly homemade, wood, leather or cloth extremities
MARK: None
SIZE: Various

---

Unmarked Pre-Greiner: Papier-mâché shoulder head; painted
    black hair, center part; vertical curls in back, pupil-less
    black glass eyes. Cloth stuffed body, leather extremities,
    dressed in good old or original clothes; all in good condition.

Size 24"    $285-325
Size 27"    $475*
*Allow extra for glass
eyes.

1970 Price Comparison
Size 16-21"   $170

Illus. No.141
Pre-Greiner--28 inch

# PRINCESS ELIZABETH
## (Mme. Alexander)

MAKER: Alexander Doll Co. of New York, N.Y., U.S.A.
DATE: 1937
MATERIAL: Composition
MARK: "Princess Elizabeth" on back of head and "Alexander
  Doll Co." underneath. Tag on clothes. (Look carefully. The
  P.E. mold was used for other Alexander Dolls.)
SIZE: Various

---

Marked Princess Elizabeth: Composition head and body, jointed
  at neck, hips and shoulders; sleep eyes, open mouth,
  original blonde mohair wig, original clothes; all in good
  condition.    Size 15-18"        $50-75
                 Size 20-24"        $75-95

1970
Price Comparison
Size 15-18"   $25

Illus. No.142. Marked
  Princess Elizabeth
in original clothes 17"

MAKER: Thought to be made by Armand Marseille of Köppelsdorf, Thüringia, Germany, for Louis Wolf & Co., Boston,
Mass. and New York, N.Y., U.S.A.

DATE: 1910

MATERIAL: Bisque head, composition ball-jointed body

MARK: "QUEEN LOUISE -- GERMANY"

SIZE: Various

---

Marked Queen Louise: Bisque socket head, ball-jointed composition body, good wig, blue, gray or brown sleep eyes; open
mouth, good clothing; entire doll in fine condition.
'Size 22-25"   $120-165

Illus. No. 143"305, Germany,
Queen Louise
10" 26 inch.

| 1970 Price Comparison |
| :---: |
| Size 18-24"   $74 |

MAKER: Th. Recknagel of Alexandrinenthal, Thüringia,
    Germany
DATE: 1909 until World War I
MATERIAL: Bisque head, composition bent-limb baby body

MARK: "R.A. and Germany" or possibly
SIZE: Various

---

R.A. Baby or Toddler: Bisque socket head; composition bent-
    limb baby or straight-leg curved-arm toddler body; sleeping
    or set eyes. Nicley dressed; all in good conditon.

Size 8"            $100-125*
*Not enough price samples
for a reliable range.

1970 Price Comparison
Size 7-12"      $40

Illus. No. 144 "Germany
R 138 A"
8" tall

MAKER: Th. Recknagel of Alexandrinenthal, Thüringia,
   Germany
DATE: 1886 to ca. World War I
MATERIAL: Bisque head, composition or wood jointed body
MARK: "R.A." with numbers and sometimes "Germany"
SIZE: Various

---

R.A. Child Doll: Marked bisque head, jointed composition or
   wooden body, set or sleep eyes, good wig; some dolls with
   molded painted shoes and socks; all in good condition.
   Size 14-16"    $100-125

Illus. No. 145
"21-Germany R2/0A"
15"

| 1970 Price Comparison |
| Size 6-15"    $33 |

MAKER: Bernard Ravca, Paris, France. Later (1939) New
York, N.Y., U.S.A.
DATE: 1924 – on
MATERIAL: Cloth with stockinet faces
MARK: Paper Label:Original Ravca Fabrication Française
SIZE: Various

---

Ravca Doll: Stockinet face individually sculpted; cloth bodies
and limbs; originally dressed; all in good condition.

|  | Size 7-1/2 to 10-1/2" |
|---|---|
| Illus.no.146.Paper Label:Original | $75-100 |
| Ravca Fabrication Française"10" | Size 18-22"   $125-150 |

# R.D. FRENCH BÉBÉ

MAKER: Rabery and Delphieu of Paris, France
DATE: 1856 (founded) to 1899 - then with S.F.B.J.
MATERIAL: Bisque head, papier-mâché body
MARK: "R. D." (from 1890)
SIZE: Various

---

Marked R. D. Bébé: Bisque head, jointed papier-mâché body,
lovely wig, paperweight eyes, closed mouth, beautifully
dressed; entire doll in nice condition. Size 20-22" $650-850
Same as above with open mouth.        Size 21-25" $345-450

| 1970 Price Comparison |
| :---: |
| Closed Mouth |
| Size 14-1/2 - 29"$275 |

Illus. No. 147 Marked
"R4 D"
28 inch

**OTTO REINECKE BENT-LIMB BABY**
**(P.M.)**

MAKER: Otto Reinecke of Hof-Moschendorf, Bavaria, Germany
DATE: 1909 on
MATERIAL: Bisque head, bent-limb composition body

MARK: "P M" also  and numbers, such as 23 and 914,
                      also Germany. (PM for Porzellan-
                      fabrik Moschendorf)
SIZE: Various

---

Marked Reinecke Baby: Bisque socket head, sleep eyes, open
    mouth, good wig, 5-piece composition bent-limb baby body.
    Dressed, all in nice condition.     Size 11-15"  $150-175
                                       Size 19-24"  $185-250

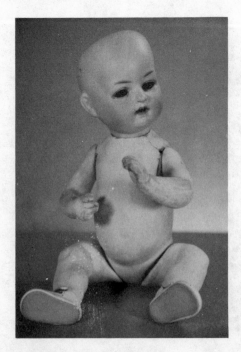

```
1970
Price Comparison
Size 11-14" $60
```

Illus. No. 148 Marked
"P. M. Grete-O"
9" (Seated)

MAKER: Mademoiselle Marie Rohmer, Paris, France
DATE: 1866 to 1880
MATERIAL: China or bisque shoulder head, jointed kid body
MARK: Oval stamp on stomach, "Mme. Rohmer-Breveté SGDG
    Paris"
SIZE: Various

---

Rohmer Fashion: China or bisque swivel shoulder head; jointed
    kid body, set glass eyes, bisque or china arms, kid or
    china legs, closed mouth, some ears pierced, lovely wig,
    fine costuming; entire doll in good condition.
    Bisque head. Size 16-18" $900-1200* (and up)
    *Not enough price samples for reliable range.
    *Allow more for china.

> 1970 Price Comparison
> Size 14-17" $642

For picture see: Collector's Encyclopedia of Dolls, Dorothy,
Elizabeth, Evelyn Coleman.  Pages 529 to 531.

# SCARLET O'HARA
### (Mme. Alexander)

MAKER: Alexander Doll Co. of New York, N.Y., U.S.A.
DATE: 1937
MATERIAL: Composition
MARK: "SCARLET O'HARA" on back of head. Also tag on
    wrist.
SIZE: Various

---

Marked Scarlet O'Hara: All composition jointed at neck,
    shoulders and hips; original wig, sleeping eyes, closed
    mouth, original clothes; entire doll in fine condition.
    Size 14-17"        $60-75

| 1970 |
| :---: |
| Price Comparison |
| Size 12-15" $37 |

Illus. No. 149. Marked
"Scarlett O'Hara"
Original Clothes
15 inch.

*Note:Scarlett is spelled
both with one "t" and
two "t's" in company
literature and on doll
identifications.

MAKER: Bruno Schmidt of Walterhausen, Thüringia, Germany
DATE: 1900 on
MATERIAL: Bisque head, composition body

MARK:  and numbers

SIZE: Various

---

Marked B.S.W. Character Baby: Bisque head, open mouth,
sleep eyes, good wig, composition bent-limb baby body;
dressed, all in good condition.    Size 12-14"      $125-195
                                   Size     24"      $265-300
So-called "Tommy Tucker". Bisque head with molded and
painted hair, winsome expression, open mouth, glass eyes.
                                   Size 14-16"      $400-500*
                                   *Not enough price
                                   samples for a reliable
                                   range.

Illus. No. 150

So-called  Tommy Tucker
24-1/2" tall.

MAKER: Franz Schmidt & Co. of Georgenthal near Waltershausen, Thüringia, Germany
DATE: Ca. 1911
MATERIAL: Bisque socket head, jointed bent-limb or toddler
   body of composition.

MARK: "F.S. & CO." "Made in Germany." Numbers such as
   1295, 1272. Deponiert included.
SIZE: Various

---

Marked F. Schmidt Doll: Bisque head, may have open nostrils,
   sleep eyes, open mouth, good wig, jointed bent-limb or
   toddler body; suitably dressed, all in good condition.

Mold # 1295:
   Size 14-16" $200-250
Mold #1272:
   Size 12-14" $250-300*
* Allow extra for solid
dome head or open-
closed mouth or #1271.

┌─────────────────────┐
│       1970          │
│  Price Comparison   │
│  Size 16-20" $90    │
└─────────────────────┘

Illus. No. 151
"F.S. & Co.
1271/32Ɀ
Germany"Deponiert
12" tall.

# SCHOENAU & HOFFMEISTER CHARACTER BABY

MAKER: Schoenau & Hoffmeister of Burggrub, Bavaria,Germany
DATE: 1910
MATERIAL: Bisque head, composition bent-limb baby body

MARK: "Porzellanfabrik Burggrub" or           , and numbers,
    such as 169, 769. Also "Hanna"
SIZE: Various

---

Marked Schoenau & Hoffmeister Baby: Bisque socket head, open
    mouth, good wig, sleep eyes, composition bent-limb baby
    body; all in good condition.      Size 14-15"    $125-195


For picture see:Collector's Encyclopedia of Dolls--Dorothy,
Elizabeth, and Evelyn Coleman.  Page 554.

MAKER: Schoenau & Hoffmeister of Burggrub, Bavaria, Germany
DATE: 1901
MATERIAL: Bisque head, composition ball-jointed body

MARK: and "Porzellanfabrik Burggrub" on head, and
numbers such as 1909, 5500, 5700

SIZE: Various

---

Schoenau & Hoffmeister Child: Bisque head, ball-jointed body,
open mouth, sleep eyes, original or good wig, original or
good clothes; all in nice condition.   Size 9-17"   $100-135
Size 22-25"   $140-185

| 1970 |
| Price Comparison |
| Size 15-23"   $42 |
| Size 25-32"   $84 |

Illus. No. 152.

" S        H-1909

Germany"
20 inches tall.

MAKER: Schoenau & Hoffmeister of Burggrub, Bavaria, Germany
DATE: After 1910
MATERIAL: Bisque head, composition body

MARK:

SIZE: Various

---

Schoenau & Hoffmeister Oriental #4900: Bisque socket head
tinted yellow, open mouth, black eyes, black mohair wig,
yellow composition ball-jointed body (five-piece body on
small sizes); Japanese outfit; all in good condition.
Size 7-1/2" $200-225*

Schoenau & Hoffmeister Hauna: Bisque socket head dark brown,
open mouth, black eyes, black mohair wig. Brown composition bent-limb body, grass skirt; all in good condition.
Size 8-9" $100-150.

*Not enough price samples to justify a reliable range.

Illus. No. 153

"S ⭐ H
4900
Germany"
7-1/2"tall
All
Original.

Illus. No. 154

"S ⭐ H
Hanna
72/0 "
All Original
7" tall

MAKER: Albert Schoenhut & Co. of Philadelphia, Penn., U.S.A.
DATE: 1911 to ca. 1930
MATERIAL: Wood, spring-jointed
MARK: "Schoenhut Doll, Pat. Jan. 17th, 1911, U.S.A."
SIZE: 14-21"
DESIGNERS: Early - Adolph Graziana; and Mr. Leslie
            Later - Harry E. Schoenhut

---

Schoenhut Child Doll: Wooden head and spring-jointed wooden
    body, marked head and/or body, original wig or good re-
    placement, brown or blue painted eyes, open/closed mouth
    with painted teeth, or closed mouth; original or suitable
    clothing, nothing repainted; all in good condition.

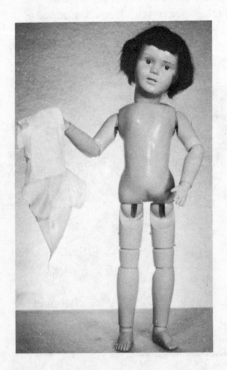

Size 14-17" $170-225
Size 21-22" $225-260*
*Allow extra for
exceptionally fine
condition and molded
hair which are both
rare.

| 1970 Price Comparison | |
|---|---|
| Size 14-17" | $75 |
| Size 20-22" | $98 |
| Molded Hair | |
| Size 14-15" | $125 |

Illus. No. 155 Marked
"Schoenhut" 18-1/2"

MAKER: Albert Schoenhut & Co. of Philadelphia, Penn.,U.S.A.
DATE: 1913-1930
MATERIAL: Wood, fully jointed toddler or bent-limb baby
    bodies
MARK: H E Schoenhut ©1913 in a circle
SIZE: 13-17"
DESIGNER: Harry E. Schoenhut

---

*Schoenhut Baby Doll: Wooden head and fully jointed toddler or
    bent-limb baby body, marked head and/or body. Painted
    hair, painted eyes, open/closed mouth, suitably dressed,
    nothing repainted; all in good condition.

Size 12-15"    $300*

    *Not enough price samples for a reliable range.
    *Also made a wooden-head Bye-lo baby with cloth body
    which is rare.

For picture see:Collector's Encyclopedia of Dolls--Dorothy,
Elizabeth and Evelyn Coleman. Page 557.

MAKER: Cameo Doll Products Co. Inc., Port Allegany, Penn., U.S.A.
DATE: Ca. 1935 - on
MATERIAL: Composition
MARK: "O'Neill" on the sole of one foot
SIZE: Seven sizes
DESIGNER: Rose O'Neill

---

Scootles: Marked, all composition, jointed at neck, shoulders and hips; blue or brown painted eyes, closed smiling mouth, molded hair, eyes to side, not dressed: doll in nice condition.　　　　　　　　　Size 15"　　　$85-90

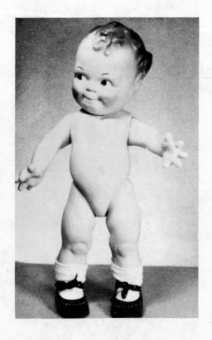

| 1970 Price Comparison |
| Size 10-15"　　$40 |

Illus. No. 156
Marked "Scootles" 15"

MAKER: Ideal Toy Corp., New York, N.Y., U.S.A.
DATE: 1934 - on
MATERIAL: Composition, jointed at neck, shoulders and hips
MARK: "SHIRLEY TEMPLE -- IDEAL" on head and torso
SIZE: 11" to 27"
DESIGNER: Bernard Lipfert

---

Marked Shirley Temple: Marked head and body, jointed composition body, all original including wig and clothes. Entire doll in good condition.

| | |
|---|---|
| Size 11" | $75-85 |
| Size 13" | $65-80 |
| Size 18" | $80-95 |
| Size 20-22" | $95-125 |

```
1970
Price Comparison
Size 12-28"    $60
```

With flirty-eyes:

| | |
|---|---|
| Size 25" | $140-165 |
| Size 27" | $195-225 |

*Allow extra for original pin or original box.

Illus. No. 157 Marked "Shirley Temple" 18 inch.

# SHIRLEY TEMPLE
## (Vinyl)

MAKER: Ideal Toy Corporation, New York, N.Y., U.S.A.
DATE: 1957
MATERIAL: Vinyl and plastic
MARK: "Ideal Doll"
     "ST-12" (Number denotes size)
SIZE: 12 - 19"

---

Ideal Shirley Temple: Vinyl and plastic, rooted hair, sleep eyes,
    jointed at shoulders and hips, original clothes; all in good
    condition.

Size    12"    $25-30
Size 15-17"    $40-45*
Size 35"  Rare
*Allow $5-10 extra for
flirty-eyes.

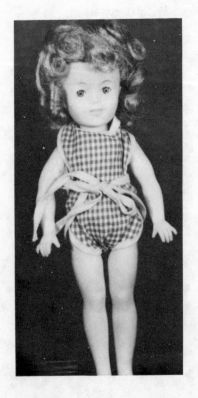

Illus. No. 158."Ideal Doll
ST-12" 12 inches
tall.

MAKER: Simon and Halbig of Gräfenhain, Thüringia, Germany
DATE: Ca. 1889's to ca. 1930's
MATERIAL: Bisque shoulder head, kid or kid and cloth body
MARK: "S & H" and/or "Simon & Halbig" with numbers such as
    1010, 949 and often "DEP" and/or "Germany"
SIZE: Various

---

S & H Shoulder Head: Marked bisque shoulder head, kid body,
  bisque arms with cloth legs, open mouth, sleep eyes, pierced
  ears, well costumed; all in nice condition.
  Size 18-21"    $135-165
  Size    30"    $250-310
  *Allow extra for swivel head on shoulder plate.

1970
Price
Comparison
Size 18-27"
$94

Illus. No. 159
"SH 1080-12-
DEP"
Shoulder Head
7-1/2 inches
tall.

# SIMON & HALBIG BABY
### (Bent-limb)

MAKER: Simon & Halbig of Gräfenhain, Thüringia, Germany
DATE: 1909 - on
MATERIAL: Bisque head, bent-limb composition body
MARK: "Simon & Halbig" and "Germany" and numbers such as
   1294
SIZE: Various

---

Marked S & H Baby: Bisque head, short curly wig of mohair,
   open mouth, sleep eyes with lashes, composition bent-limb
   baby body; nicely dressed; all in very good condition.
   Size 16-22"          $295

> 1970
> Price
> Comparison
> Size 20-24"
> $145

Illus. No.160
"Simon &
Halbig
1294
Germany"
16" tall.

MAKER: Simon & Halbig of Gräfenhain, Thüringia, Germany

DATE: Ca. 1880's

MATERIAL: Bisque socket head on ball-jointed wood and composition body or shoulder head on jointed kid body with bisque lower arms

MARK: "S & H" or "Simon & Halbig" with numbers, such as 949, 950, 939, etc.

SIZE: Various

---

Marked S & H Child: Bisque head, paperweight eyes, closed mouth, pierced ears, good wig, dressed; body as above in good condition.    Size 16-19"    $350-450

Size    24"    $500-600

Illus.
No. 61
949
S & H
19" tall

# SIMON & HALBIG CHILD DOLL
## (Composition Body)

MAKER: Simon and Halbig of Gräfenhain, Thüringia, Germany

DATE: At least from 1889 into the 1930's; probably earlier but no documented proof as yet

MATERIAL: Bisque head, composition ball-jointed body; sometimes French type, part wood

MARK: "S & H" and/or "Simon & Halbig" with numbers, such as 1079, 1039, 550, 1249, 1009, and often "DEP" and/or "Germany"

SIZE: Various

---

Marked S & H Child: Bisque head, good wig, original ball-jointed composition and wood body; sleep eyes, open mouth, pierced ears, very pretty clothes; all in nice condition.

Size 17-18"  $140-150*

Size 20-24"  $150-185*

Size 26-30"  $250-325*

> 1970 Price Comparison
> Size 21-38"  $88

Mold #1249 Santa: Size 18-26" $185-275*

*Allow extra for #1279, #1299 and Flirty-eyes or walking types.

Illus. No. 162 "Halbig S&H Germany 7" 18 inches tall.

Illus. No. 163 "1079-2- DEP SH Germany" 11" tall.

### (Closed Mouth)

MAKER:Simon & Halbig of Gräfenhain, Thüringia, Germany
DATE: Ca. 1900
MATERIAL: Bisque head, kid body with bisque hands.
MARK: "S & H   1160"
SIZE: Various

---

Marked S & H 1160(So-called Little Women type):Shoulder head
with closed mouth on kid or cloth body with bisque lower
arms and legs.                          Size 9"    $110-135

For picture see: Collector's Encyclopedia of Dolls--Dorothy,
Elizabeth, and Evelyn Coleman. Pages 574-575.

MAKER: Simon & Halbig of Gräfenhain, Thüringia, Germany
DATE: Ca. 1910
MATERIAL: Bisque socket head, composition lady body, molded
    bust, slim-type arms and legs
MARK: "S & H 1159"
SIZE: Various

---

Marked S & H 1159 lady doll: Bisque socket head, open mouth,
    good wig, pierced ears, sleep eyes, lady body as above,
    elegantly dressed; all in good condition.
    Size 18-20"    $425-495
    Size 22-24"    $600-650

Illus. No. 164.
"1159 Germany Halbig
S&H"
15inches tall.

MAKER: Simon and Halbig of Gräfenhain, Thüringia, Germany
DATE: Ca. 1889 into 1930's
MATERIAL: Bisque head, jointed composition body with painted
    shoes and socks or composition ball-jointed body.
MARK: "S&H and/or "SIMON & HALBIG" with numbers, such as
    1039 and 1078, and often "DEP" and/or "Germany"
SIZE: 6-12"

---

Tiny Marked S & H: Bisque head, composition body of five
    pieces, open mouth, nice wig, sleep eyes, original clothes;
    all in good condition.       Size   6-8-1/2"    $65-100*

            * Allow extra for
            flirty-eyes or
            completely ball-
            jointed body.

| 1970 |
| :---: |
| Price |
| Comparison |
| Size 6-12"     $40 |

Illus. No. 165
Marked
"S&H-1078"
Original    Clothes
8 inches.

**SKIPPY**
(EFFanBEE)

MAKER: EFFanBEE Doll Corporation (Bernard Fleischaker &
    Hugo Baum), New York, N.Y., U.S.A.
DATE: Ca. 1926
MATERIAL: Composition
MARK: "EFFanBEE SKIPPY ©️ P.L.CROSBY"
SIZE: 14 inches
DESIGNER: P. L. Crosby

---

Skippy Marked Head and Shoulders: All composition, jointed at
    neck, hips and shoulders; painted eyes to side, dressed;
    in good condition.                    Size 14"        $55-65

| 1970 Price Comparison |
| :---: |
| Size 14"        $30 |

Illus. No. 166
"Effanbee Skippy
©️
P. L. Crosby"

# SKOOKUM INDIAN DOLL
**(McAboy)**

MAKER: H.H. Tammen Co., New York, N.Y., Denver, Colorado and Los Angeles, California, U.S.A.
DATE: 1913 - on
MATERIAL: Composition or celluloid type mask faces;excelsior stuffed cloth bodies; wooden legs, composition feet
MARK: Sometimes marked "SKOOKUMS" on sole of foot
SIZE: 3" to 42"
DESIGNER and ORIGINATOR: Mary McAboy, Denver, Colorado

---

SKOOKUM Indian Doll: Indian blanket clad doll - folds in blanket represent arms; mask face, cotton print dress or cotton shirt and felt trousers, eyes to side, black hair, head band with one or more feathers; beads etc., all very colorful, in good condition.

| | |
|---|---|
| Size 10-12" | $25-35 |
| Size 15-19" | $60-65 |

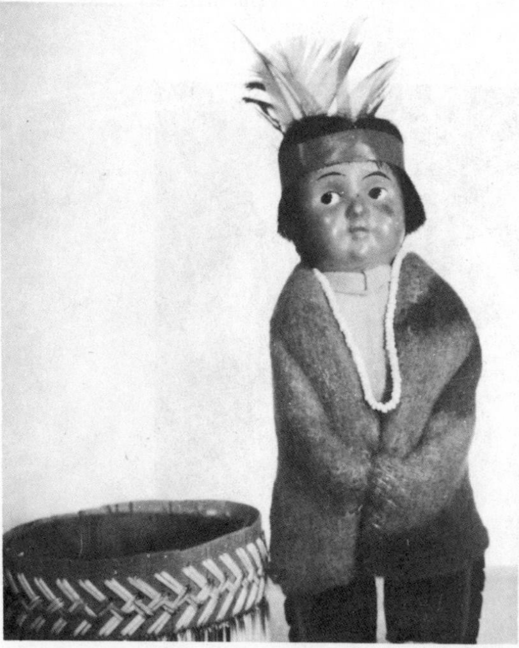

1970
Price
Comparison
Size 6-1/2-24"
$15

Illus. No. 167
Skookum
Indian Boy
6-1/2 inch.

MAKER: Société Française de Fabrication de Bébés & Jouets,
     Paris, France
DATE: 1910 - on
MATERIAL: Bisque head, ball-jointed composition body
MARK: "S.F.B.J. Paris" also #'s 226, 227, 235, 237, etc.
SIZE: Various

---

S.F.B.J. Character Child: Marked bisque head with molded
     and painted hair or flocked hair or good wig; paperweight
     eyes, open/closed or open mouth, ball-jointed composition
     body, nicely dressed; all in good condition.
     Size 14-16"   $1,000 and up.*
     *Not enough price samples to justify a reliable range.

     Illus. No. 168. Left doll: "SFBJ 227 Paris" 14" tall. Ball-
         jointed body.
     Right doll: "227" 13-1/2 inch tall. Straight-limbed body.

MAKER: Société Française de Fabrication de Bébés & Jouets,
   Paris, France
DATE: 1899 - on
MATERIAL: Bisque head, jointed papier-mâché body
MARK: "SFBJ Paris"
SIZE: Various

---

S.F.B.J. Child Doll: Marked bisque head, jointed composition
   body, pierced ears, sleep eyes, open mouth, good French
   wig, nicely dressed; all in good condition.  18-22"  $250-300

Illus. No. 169
"SFBJ Paris"
20" tall.

# S.F.B.J. CHILD DOLL
## (#251)

MAKER: Société Française de Fabrication de Bébés & Jouets,
Paris, France
DATE: 1910 - on
MATERIAL: Bisque head, papier-mâché body (toddler or baby
body)
MARK: "S.F.B.J. #251, Paris"
SIZE: Various

---

S.F.B.J. #251-1: Marked bisque head, papier-mâché (toddler
or baby) body, sleep eyes, open mouth, good wig, well
dressed; all in nice condition.     Size 16-19"    $500-600

Marked   Unis France
#251
Size 12-15"    $350-400

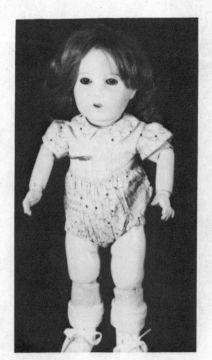

| 1970 Price Comparison | |
|---|---|
| Size 10-22" | $111 |
| Size 24-28" | $150 |

Illus. No. 170
"Unis France 251 21-149"
13-1/2" tall  Toddler body
(The Unis mark is later
than the SFBJ mark, but it
is the same mold).

MAKER: Société Française de Fabrication de Bébés & Jouets,
   Paris, France
DATE: 1899 - on
MATERIAL: Bisque head, jointed papier-mâché body (Adult
   body very rare)
MARK: "S.F.B.J. Paris --- #60" (or #301)
SIZE: Various

---

S.F.B.J. #60 or #301 Child Doll: Marked bisque head, jointed
   papier-mâché body, set or sleep eyes, good French wig,
   open mouth, pierced ears, well costumed; all in nice condition.                                          Size 18-22"    $250-300

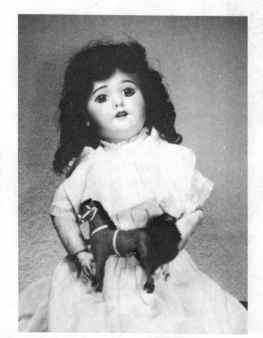

1970
Price
Comparison
Size 13-15-1/2"
$94
Size 18-24" $123

Illus. No. 171
"S.F.B.J. #60 Paris"
20 inch.

MAKER: Société Française de Fabrication de Bébés & Jouets,
    Paris, France
DATE: Ca. 1900 - on
MATERIAL: Bisque head, papier-mâché body
MARK: "S. F. B. J. Paris" with 60 or 301. Also "Unis France"
SIZE: Usually 12" and under

---

S. F. B. J. Costume Doll: Marked bisque head, five-piece
    composition body (sometimes completely jointed); original
    wig, glass eyes, open or closed mouth, original costume;
    all in good condition.        Size 6- 8"    $75-100
                                   Size 10-12"   $125-150

Illus. No. 172   "France
SFBJ 301 Paris"
12 inches tall.
All original costume.
(This particular doll has a
composition head, and would
be priced accordingly.)

MAKER: Société Française de Fabrication de Bébés & Jouets,
    Paris, France
DATE: 1905 - on
MATERIAL: Bisque head, papier-mâché body
MARK: "S.F.B.J. Paris" and sometimes #60 or #301
SIZE: Various

---

S.F.B.J. Walking-& Kiss-Throwing: Marked bisque head,
    composition body with straight legs, walking mechanism at
    top, hand raises to throw a kiss, head moves from side to
    side, eyes flirt, glass eyes, good wig, open mouth, pierced
    ears, nicely dressed; all in working order.

                                    Size 20-22"    $350-425

Illus. No. 173
"Deposé
SFBJ
9"
22 inches tall.
Walks, throws kisses
& flirts.

# S.F.B.J. LAUGHING CHILD
## (#236)

MAKER: Société Française de Fabrication de Bébés & Jouets,
    Paris, France
DATE: 1910 - on
MATERIAL: Bisque head, papier-mâché body; jointed toddler
    or bent-limb baby
MARK: "S.F.B.J. -- #236 -- Paris"
SIZE: Various

---

S.F.B.J. #236: Marked bisque head, chubby body of papier-
    mâché, original or good wig, smiling open/closed mouth,
    blue or brown sleep eyes, cute clothes; all in good
    condition. Size  9-12"  $350-400
                Size 14-18"  $425-495
                Size 26-27"     $650

| 1970 Price Comparison | |
| --- | --- |
| Size 16-20" | $228 |
| Size 21-26" | $258 |

Illus. No. 174
"SFBJ 236  Paris"
15" jointed toddler  body.

MAKER: Société Française de Fabrication de Bébés & Jouets,
    Paris, France
DATE: 1910 - on
MATERIAL: Bisque head, papier-mâché jointed toddler body
MARK: "S.F.B.J. #252 -- Paris"
SIZE: Various.

---

Marked S.F.B.J. #252: Bisque head, open mouth, good wig,
    sleep eyes, jointed toddler body, dressed; all in very nice
    condition. $2,000-3,000*
    *Not enough price samples to justify a reliable range.

> 1970
> Price
> Comparison
> Size 14-36" $189

Illus. No. 175
Right doll: SFBJ
Toddler
(Unidentified)
28" tall
Left doll: "SFBJ
252 Paris 12"
27-1/2 "tall.

# S.F.B.J. TWIRP
## (#247)

MAKER: Société Française de Fabrication de Bébés & Jouets,
   Paris, France
DATE: After 1910 - on
MATERIAL: Bisque head, papier-mâché body, bent-limb or
   toddler
MARK: "S. F. B. J.   PARIS  #247"
SIZE: Various

---

Marked S. F. B. J. #247: Marked bisque head, papier-mâché
   body, good wig, sleep eyes, closed or open/closed mouth;
   suitably dressed; all in nice condition.
   Size 14-18"    $800-1,000
   Size 20-25"  $1,100-1,300

```
1970
Price Comparison
Size 7-13" $117
```

Illus. No. 176
"SFBJ
247
Paris"
21" tall
Jointed toddler body.

MAKER: Alexander Doll Co., Inc., New York, N.Y., U.S.A.
DATE: 1939
MATERIAL: Composition, jointed at neck, shoulders and hips
MARK: "Madame Alexander -- Sonja Henie" embossed on back
    of neck or on shoulders
SIZE: 14", 18", 21"

---

Marked Sonja Henie: All composition, jointed as above; smiling
    open mouth  with teeth, sleep eyes, lovely human hair wig,
    original clothes and shoe skates; all in very nice condition.
    Size 14"        $65- 95
    Size 18-22"    $100-125

     Illus. No. 177
   "Madame Alexander
     Sonja Henie"
    18inches tall.

> 1970 Price Comparison
>   Size 15-18"   $44

# JULES STEINER BÉBÉ

MAKER: Jules Nicholas Steiner (and successors), Paris, France
DATE: 1870's to ca. 1908
MATERIAL: Bisque head, jointed papier-mâché body
MARK: (In part) "LE PARISIEN--PARIS", "BÉBÉ LE
    PARISIEN", "BÉBÉ STEINER", "STEINER S.G.D.G.",
    "BÉBÉ PHÉNIX" etc.
SIZE: Various

---

Steiner Bébé: Marked bisque head, jointed papier-mâché body,
    good French wig, closed or open mouth (teeth upper and
    lower); beautiful paperweight eyes (some controlled by
    wires); lovely clothes; all in nice condition.

                        15-18" $650- 850
                        21-22" $900-1,200

| 1970 |
| :---: |
| Price |
| Comparison |
| Size 16-20" |
| $328 |

Illus. No. 178
"Steiner BTE
S.G.D.G. S^{te} C.G.
Bourgoin"
28 inch.

MAKER: Unknown German firms

DATE: Ca. 1870 - on

MATERIAL: Composition head, cloth body, cloth or kid
extremities

MARK: Label "M & S SUPERIOR 2015" or "G. L. 2015 SUPER-
IOR PERFECTLY HARMLESS" or " M & S SUPERIOR
4515," etc. Later ones also marked "Germany"

SIZE: Various

---

Superior Doll: Label on back of shoulder head; papier-mâché
shoulder head, black or blond molded painted hair; original
cloth body, old kid arms and boots, quaint old clothing,
brown or blue painted eyes; all in nice condition.

| | | |
|---|---|---|
| Size 17-18" | | $85-125 |
| Size | 28" | $200-250 |

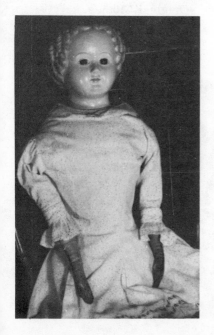

```
1970 Price Comparison
Size 18-28"    $80
```

Illus. No. 179 Unmarked
M&S Superior type
28" tall

MAKER: TERRI LEE Sales Corp., V. Gradwohl, Pres., U.S.A.
DATE: 1946 - Lincoln, Nebraska; then Apple Valley, California
    from 1951 to ca. 1962.
MATERIAL: Celanese Plastic (hard plastic)
MARK: "TERRI LEE" embossed across shoulders
SIZE: 16 inch only

---

Terri Lee Child Doll: 16" marked; all original including
    clothing and accessories; jointed at neck, shoulders and
    hips. Mint condition.       Size 16"      $35-45

| 1970 Price Comparison |
|---|
| Mint $20 |

Illus. No. 180 Shelf
Group of Terri Lee
Dolls
Original Clothes.

MAKER: Perhaps Carl Bergner of Sonneberg, Thüringia, Germany

DATE: Early 20th Century

MATERIAL: Bisque head with three faces, cloth torso, composition arms & cap.

MARK: "C.B" on back shoulder

SIZE: Smaller, such as 11" and 13"

---

MARKED "C.B" Multi-face: Bisque head with three different faces(usually sleeping, laughing, and crying). Dressed. All in good condition.  Size 11-13"   $1,050-1,200.

Illus.No.181
Multiface doll
marked "C.B"
12" tall.

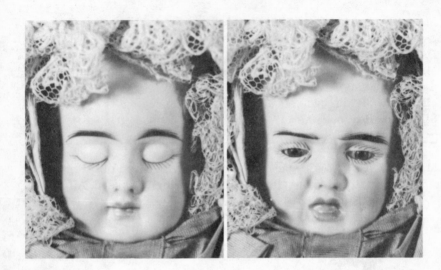

Illus. Nos. 182, 183, 184
Multiface Doll
marked "C.B"
12" tall.
The close-up
pictures show the
different faces.

MAKER: Terri Lee Sales Corp., Apple Valley, California, U.S.A.
DATE: Early 1950's
MATERIAL: Celanese Plastic (hard plastic)
MARK: On back of neck or between shoulders
SIZE: 10 inch only

---

Tiny Terri Lee: Marked and completely original, jointed at neck, hips and shoulders. Mint condition.
Size 10"          $25-35

Illus. No. 185 Marked
"Tiny Jerri
&
Terri Lee"
Original Clothes.
10 inches.

| 1970 Price Comparison |
| Size 10"     $15 |

182 **TRUDY**
(Three-faced Doll)

MAKER: Three-in-One Doll Corporation, New York, N.Y.,
    U.S.A.
DATE: 1946
MATERIAL: Composition head, arms and legs; cloth body
MARK: On clothing (see below)
SIZE: Various

---

Trudy, Three-faced Doll: Composition head, arms and legs,
    cloth body, composition knob on top of head which turns
    faces, original dress and bonnet marked: "Sleepy Trudy,
    Smily Trudy, Weepy Trudy" in tiny pastel circles printed on
    white dress material. All fine condition.
    Size 14-16"  $65-75

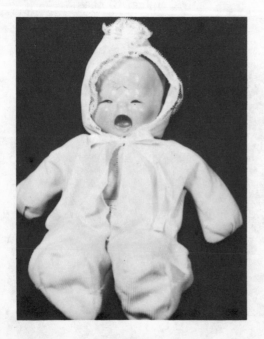

> 1970
> Price
> Comparison
> Size 14-18"  $34

Illus. No. 186
Unmarked Trudy
Showing "Weepy"
face
New clothes. 14"tall.

MAKER: Société Française de Fabrication de Bébés et Jouets.
  (S.F.B.J.) of Paris and Montruil-sous-Bois, France
DATE: 1899 - on
MATERIAL: Bisque head, jointed papier-mâché body
MARK:    ⟨UNIS⟩        Also "Unis France 71  149  301"
         ⟨FRANCE⟩         "71 Unis France 149  60"
SIZE: Various

---

Unis Child Doll: Marked bisque head, papier-mâché body or
  wood and papier-mâché jointed body; sleep eyes, good wig,
  pretty clothes, pierced ears, open mouth; all in nice condition.         Mold#301 or #60 Child:Size  5- 7"  $85-115
                                   Size 14-19" $145-225
                                   Size 31-36" $450-500

1970 Price Comparison
Size 6-1/2-12"    $75
Size 17-26"       $113

Illus.No.187 Marked
"Unis France-
301"on head
also
"Au Nain Bleu" tag label
on wrist. All original.
5 inches.

**WALKÜRE CHILD DOLL**
**(K & H)**

MAKER: Kley and Hahn of Ohrdruf, Thüringia, Germany
DATE: Ca. 1902 - on
MATERIAL: Bisque head, composition ball-jointed body
MARK: "Walküre - K & H Germany" etc.
SIZE: Various

---

Walküre Doll: Marked bisque head, ball-jointed composition
body, good wig, open mouth, pierced ears, blue or brown
sleep eyes; well dressed, all in nice condition.
Size 23-25"    $150-195
Size 27-30"    $250-325

> 1970
> Price
> Comparison
> Size 16-27"   $82

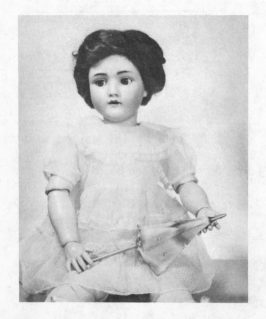

Illus. No. 188
"Walküre-Germany
76"
30 inches

## (Montanari or Pierotti Type)

MAKER: Unknown firms of England, Germany and France
DATE: Mid-19th century through the early 1900's
MATERIAL: Wax head, arms and legs; cloth body
MARK: None
SIZE: Various

---

Unmarked Poured Wax Doll: Head, lower arms and legs of wax; cloth body, blue or brown glass eyes, blond or brown set-in hair; original clothes or very well dressed; all in good condition. Size 16-24"   $325-425*
*Allow extra for signed Pierotti, Montanari or Mrs. Peck.
Same as above with wig(instead of set-in hair)
Size 20-28" $225-325.

| 1970 Price Comparison | |
| --- | --- |
| Size 10-18" | $127 |
| Size 22-32" | $162 |

Illus. No. 189 Poured
Wax-20 inch
All Original.

MAKERS: Numerous firms in England, Germany, or France
DATE: During the 1800's
MATERIAL: Wax over shoulder head of some type of composition or papier-mâché; cloth body; wax over composition or wooden limbs.
MARK: None
SIZE: Various

---

Bonnet Wax Doll: Ca. 1860 to 1880: Wax over shoulder head, original cloth body and wooden extremities; blue, brown or black set eyes; nice old clothes. All in good condition.
Size 20"$200*
*Not enough price samples to justify a reliable range.
Pumpkin Head Doll: Ca. 1850 to 1890: Wax over shoulder head, molded band in molded blond hair pompadour, original cloth body, black, blue or brown glass sleep or set eyes; wax over or wooden extremities with molded socks or boots, nice old clothes, not rewaxed. All in good condition.
Size 13-17"       $125
Size 24-25"    $165-235
Wax Doll with wig: Ca. mid-19th century into early twentieth century; wax over shoulder head, not rewaxed, original cloth body, blond or brown human hair or mohair wig, blue, brown or black glass eyes, sleep or set; open or closed mouth, any combination of extremities mentioned above; also arms may be made of china. Original clothing or suitably dressed; entire doll in nice condition.
Size 16-19" $125-160
Size 22-24" $175-200*
*Allow extra for a fashion-type body.

| 1970 Price Comparison | | |
|---|---|---|
| Bonnet Wax Doll. | Size 10-26" | $105 |
| Pumpkin Head Doll. | Size 15-18" | $ 65 |
| Wax Doll with wig. | Size 14-26" | $ 75 |

Illus. No. 190
"Wax Over" with
Wig on Cloth
Body
Composition Arms
and
Legs.
16 inch.

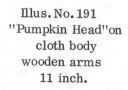

Illus. No. 191
"Pumpkin Head" on
cloth body
wooden arms
11 inch.

MAKER: Victoria Toy Works, Wellington, Shropshire, England,
    for Norah Wellings
DATE: 1926 to ca. 1960
MATERIAL: Fabric: felt, velvet and velour etc. Stuffed.
MARK: On tag on foot: "Made in England by Norah Wellings"
SIZE: Various - thousands sold on English ships
DESIGNER: Norah Wellings

---

Wellings Sailor Boy: Stitch jointed at shoulders and hips; head
    swivels somewhat from left to right. Body and extremities
    made of stuffed dark blue velvet; shoes of black velvet
    (marked on one sole), face molded and covered with flesh
    colored stockinette; painted features, eyes to side. Wears
    white sailor cap with name of ship on black band. "H.M.S.
    Queen Mary". White cord around neck, light blue collar.
    Fingers stitched, hands of flesh colored cotton cloth. All in
    good shape.                    Size 8-12"          $15-20

1970
Price
Comparison
Size 8-13"   $14

Illus. No. 192
Marked
"Norah Wellings"
All Original
8 inch

MAKER: Alexander Doll Co. of New York, N.Y., U.S.A.
DATE: 1938
MATERIAL: All composition, jointed at waist, neck, shoulders and hips
MARK: Embossed on back of body: "Wendy-Ann - Mme. Alexander - New York, N.Y."
SIZE: 13-1/2 inches

---

Wendy-Ann: Composition doll, jointed as above; nicely dressed, sleep eyes, closed mouth, beautiful human hair wig; all in very good condition.   Size 13-1/2"   $50-60

| 1970 Price Comparison |
| :---: |
| Size 13-1/2"   $25 |

Illus. No. 193
"Wendy-Ann
Mme. Alexander
New York"
13-1/2"   tall

# WISLIZENUS DOLL
## (A.W.)

MAKER: Adolf Wislizenus of Waltershausen, Thüringia, Germany.
DATE: About 1890 - on
MATERIAL: Bisque head, composition ball-jointed body
MARK: "A.W.", "A.W." over "W", "A.W. SPECIAL", sometimes with "Germany" added, sometimes "OLD GLORY", etc.
SIZE: Various

---

Wislizenus Doll: Marked bisque head, composition ball-jointed body, blue or brown sleep eyes, open mouth, good wig, dressed. All in nice condition.      Size 19-27"    $125-175

1970
Price
Comparison
Size 21-26"  $65

Illus. No. 194
Marked
"A.W. Special
2"
22 inch
Doll in Arms--
Mme. Alexander
"Wendy"
8 inch.

194                    **INDEX**